The 'Gig Do

Dr William Irvine
&
The Irvine Memorial Hospital

by

Rita Isles

To Marjorie & Bruce
from Rita

TIPPERMUIR
· BOOKS LIMITED ·

The 'Gig Docter o Athole'.
Dr William Irvine & The Irvine Memorial Hospital

This first edition published and copyright 2019 by
Tippermuir Books Ltd, Perth, Scotland.
mail@tippermuirbooks.co.uk
www.tippermuirbooks.co.uk

Editorial and Project Director: Paul S. Philippou.
© Tippermuir
Photographs: The 'Author's Collection'.

Map: Rob Hands
Cover design: Matthew Mackie.
Text design, layout and artwork:
Bernard Chandler [graffik]

ISBN: 978-1-9164778-4-1 (paperback).
A CIP catalogue record for this book is available from the British Library.

Text set in Palatino LT Std 10.5/14pt.
Printed and bound by CPI Group (UK) Ltd, Croydon, CR0 4YY.

ACKNOWLEDGEMENTS

A very big thankyou goes to everyone who has provided me with information and photographs.

My deepest regret is that Ruby Ripley died before I completed this book. Ruby, the retired Matron of Irvine Memorial Hospital, wanted the hospital and Dr Irvine to be remembered.

I cannot tell how the truth may be:
I say the tale as 'twas telt to me.

NOTES

i. A 'gig' is historically a light, two-wheeled carriage pulled by a horse.

ii. Pitlochry's hospital was known as the Irvine Memorial Nursing Home up to 1946 when it was officially changed to Irvine Memorial Cottage Hospital. Cottage however appears to have fallen out of usage immediately; and over the next few years, the hospital was often referred to as the Irvine Memorial Home. From the establishment of the NHS in 1948, Irvine Memorial Hospital became customary.

CONTENTS

LIST OF ILLUSTRATIONS

Map of Pitlochry.

Chapter 1 - Dr William Stewart Irvine – 'The Old Doctor'
The young William Stewart Irvine.
'The Gig Docter'.
Pitlochry's main street in the early 1870s.
William Stewart Irvine's gravestone.
Dr William Stewart Irvine in later life.

Chapter 2 - Dr Robert William Irvine: 'Dr Bob'
Robert William Irvine.
Rosehill, Pitlochry.
Scotland beat England at Raeburn Place, 1871.
Scotland's International Rugby Team, 1871. Robert 'Bulldog' Irvine
    stands 5th from the left in the middle row.
Robert Irvine's grave, Dysart Cemetery, Pitlochry.
Census Information About the Residents at Craigatin.

Chapter 3 - Henrietta Caroline McInroy: 13 June 1828 to 15 January 1898
Lude House, Blair Atholl.
Charles McInroy.
'A Century of Community Caring' Christmas Card, 1989.
Kilmaveonaig Kirkyard, Blair Atholl.
Henrietta McInroy's gravestone in Kilmaveonaig Kirkyard.
Notes on The McInroy Family Tree.
The McInroy Family Tree.

Chapter 4 - Miss Emma Molyneux (Molyneux meaning 'Little Mills')
Tom-na-Monachan.
Portrait of Emma Molyneux (signature inset).
Emma Molyneux's Headstone: 'In Memory of Emma Molyneux,
    Daughter of the Late John Blayds Molyneux, Lady of Grace of the
    Order of St John of Jerusalem in England Died 11th August 1936.
    By the Faith of Jesus Christ – Blessed Hope.'
The Pine Trees Hotel, Pitlochry, formerly Tom-na-Monachan.
The Molyneux Family Tree.
Selected Timeline for the Parish of Moulin, 1832-92.

Chapter 5 - The Story of the Irvine Memorial Hospital – 1901–2018
The Irvine Memorial Nursing Home, 1902.
Lady Helen Stewart Murray, 1916.

David Alexander Tod, 1916.

Pitlochry Town Hall.

January 1980. Presentation of a defibrillator machine, the money
for which was raised through community efforts.

Matron Ruby Ripley and some of her staff, 1979–80.

Pupils of Pitlochry High School presenting 'Lifting Belts', 1989.

Presentation of a cheque from the Atholl Highlanders to Friends of
Irvine Memorial Hospital at Blair Castle, May 1991.

Dr Trevor Ross with Emergency Medical Vehicle, *c*.1990.

Staff group 1, 2002.

Staff group 2, 2002.

The Irvine Memorial Hospital Garden in winter, 2002.

Irvine Memorial Hospital Centenary Christmas card, 2002.

Opening of the new Pitlochry Community Hospital by
Nicola Sturgeon, Health Minister, 19 August 2008.

Chapter 6 - *Memories and Staff Experiences of Irvine Memorial Hospital
and the Various Hospital Units*

The Reverend Bill Shannon (chaplain, 1991-8).

'A Thank You Poem' by May Scott – patient.

Chapter 7 - *The Ambulance Service, Toberargan Surgery, Doctors and
Chemists in the Atholl Area, Senior Nursing Staff, the Irving Memorial
Hanging, Tablecloths*

The Irvine Memorial Hanging.

Small tablecloth presented to Matron Ruby Ripley on her retirement, 1989.

Large tablecloth presented to Matron Ruby Ripley on her retirement, 1989.

Chapter 8 - *Chequers Residential Care Home, the Tryst Day Centre,
Pitlochry Senior Citizens Good Neighbour Association, and Bobbin Mill*

Chequers Residential Care Home, 1966-2009.

Patchwork Costume parade 2003. From left: Fiona McPherson with
daughters Iona and Caroline, and Donald Isles.

'The First Bus', 12th July 1980.

'Presenting the First Bus' - L to R: Bill Shannon (Secretary) and
Dr David Cruikshank (Chairman).

'The Third Bus' - Ruby Ripley (Matron) and Ian Mcintosh (driver)
receiving the bus at the Irvine Memorial Hospital *c*.1987.

'The Second to Last Bus', February 2010 – David Clark (John R. Weir)
and Donald Isles (Chairman).

PREFACE

I arrived in Pitlochry in January 1979 in the snow. The A9 still came through the centre of Kindallachan, Ballinluig, Pitlochry, Blair Atholl, and all places north. Pitlochry was then a small community, with many local residents born and brought up in the area.

There were many places of employment: The Hydro Board, Forestry Commission, and Water Board, as well the gasworks, police, Fishery Board for Scotland Freshwater Fisheries Laboratory. And many various shops and small businesses provided all the community's basic needs and more, as they would send away for anything they did not have to hand. There were many tradespeople: builders, joiners, plumbers, electricians, TV engineers, painters, and many more clever people doing jobs that are now lost.

So, I was surprised to hear many people saying that Pitlochry did not have a history, *"it is just a Victorian Town"*, they would say. I thought this was a strange notion and have discovered how wrong they were, especially as in the past the area included numerous small hamlets whose buildings left their mark on the land, long before the arrival of the Victorians.

The modern prosperity of Pitlochry does of course date from about 1844 when Queen Victoria enjoyed a refreshment at the *Moulinearn Inn* en route to Blair Castle. Sir James Clark, the royal physician, formed such a high opinion of the air and climate of the area, that, after he travelled to Pitlochry with Queen Victoria, he began to prescribe to his patients a holiday here. Sir James Simpson, the famous Edinburgh doctor, was also convinced of the splendid climate of Pitlochry. Visitors had already been attracted prior to this, partly owing to the praise given to Pitlochry by J. D. McCulloch in his writings.

Working as a hairdresser and enjoying history, it was ideal to chat with the locals about the past that they could recall – it proved very interesting and rewarding as I wrote down so many bits of information and kept a file, not realising how useful this information would be. Sadly, so many of those who related events are now long gone, so I hope in this book I have included all the relevant interesting memories so many gave me.

In the mid-1990s, I joined the Victorian Festival Committee, which was put together by the Tourist Association and chaired by Peter Crerar of Blair Athol Distillery, Pitlochry. It was a huge undertaking on everyone's part; all came together well, and all participated in all that happened, including dressing up in costumes from the late-nineteenth and early twentieth centuries.

It was at this point, I realised I had a tremendous amount of information on this period, especially for putting together a fund-raising event. The committee decided to have an event in the style of a Victorian afternoon tea, with music, song, and stories in costume, in the Green Park Hotel, whose owners kindly gave us the use of their ground floor rooms and garden,

I had a very enjoyable task of compiling information about seven persons of note in the past who were connected with Pitlochry:

Dr William Irvine of Pitlochry.

Henrietta McInroy of Lude House, Blair Atholl.

Emma Molyneux of Pine Trees.

Professor John Stewart Blackie of Edinburgh
     who holidayed in Pitlochry.

Beatrix Potter who holidayed in Birnam.

Robert Louis Stevenson who holidayed in Moulin.

Queen Victoria who visited Pitlochry.

In putting together their stories, I discovered how useful was the information I had gathered over time, and how useful it could be in putting together the story of Dr William Irvine and the Irvine Memorial Hospital. In the early 1980s, I walked right into the clutches of Matron Ruby Ripley when, talking casually at an early fund-raising event for the senior citizens bus, I mentioned the information I had. A collusion was formed, but little did I realise I would be the sole compiler of this book on the hospital and Dr William Irvine.

Thus, follows the history of places, times, developments, and people who brought Pitlochry forward from three semi-isolated hamlets and how they all played their part in Dr William Irvine's life and the Irvine Memorial Hospital.

Rita Isles, 2019

Map of
PITLOCHRY
SHOWING MAIN LOCATIONS REFERRED TO

1 IRVINE MEMORIAL HOSPITAL

2 TOBERARGAN SURGERY

3 OLD AMBULANCE STATION

4 TRYST

5 CHEQUERS

6 BOBBIN MILL –
    6a Community Hospital
    6b New Surgery
    6c New Ambulance Station
    6d Balhousie Care Home

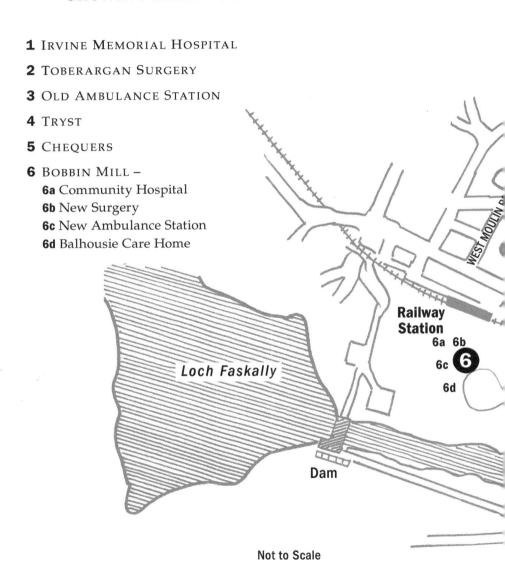

Loch Faskally

WEST MOULIN R...

Railway Station
6a 6b
6c **6**
6d

Dam

Not to Scale

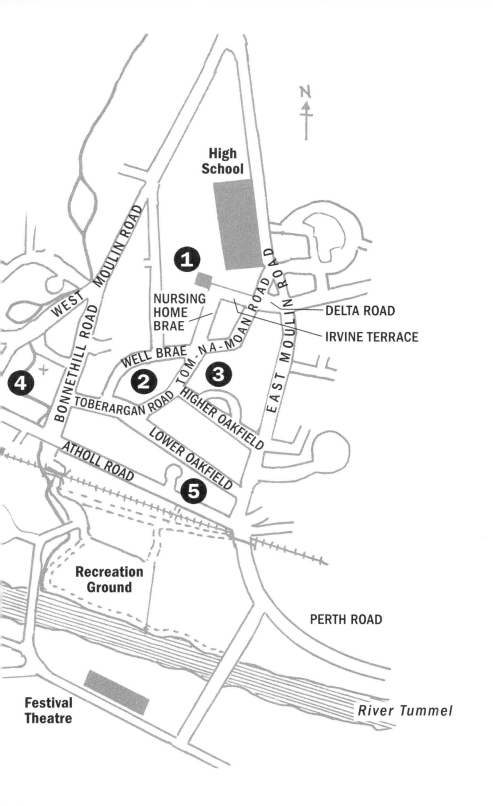

CHAPTER ONE

Dr William Stewart Irvine –
'The Old Doctor'

D R WILLIAM STEWART IRVINE was born on 28th May 1812, the fourth child of seven to Janet (Jessie) Stewart and Alexander Irvine, minister at Little Dunkeld from 1806 to 1824. He was baptised in Dunkeld on 7th June 1812 and was educated at Dunkeld Grammar School, after which he attended the University of Glasgow. There he gained his LFPS (1832) and his MD (1833). William Irvine was bestowed FRCS in Edinburgh in 1839 at 27 years of age.

The young William Stewart Irvine.

It is interesting to note that during Dr Irvine's student days, town councils sold the bodies of paupers and criminals to the medical schools. There were however never enough bodies, so any student producing a body for anatomical dissection was excused the fees for his anatomy class, and so the practice of grave robbing began, leading to the notorious exploits of Burke and Hare.

In the days before 1833, when Dr Irvine moved back to Perthshire to begin his practice, it was a case of coaching, riding, or walking – there were no railways or bicycles. The health of the people of Strathtay was looked after by a Dr Stewart, who had a small estate in the Strath and was known as Dr Findynate after his property. This old gentleman was a typical Highlander. In his early life, he had entered the Royal Navy as a surgeon's assistant, for he never acquired any qualifications of any kind. After leaving the Royal Navy and returning to Strathtay, Findynate practised medicine for many miles around. He drove around the countryside in an old-fashioned gig, taking with him a large medicine chest.

The 'Gig Docter'.

When visiting a patient, Dr Findynate never hurried: if he considered a case a serious one, he just remained until the patient died or recovered. If it should take a few days or a week, time was of no importance. If anyone else wanted him during his absence from home, a messenger was sent, whereupon he would get in his gig and jog along to the next place, perhaps to remain a few days if necessary before he went home or on to another place. This old gentleman gave up the practice in 1858 when the Medical Act came into force; he died soon after.

Dr Irvine's immediate predecessor in Pitlochry and district was a Dr Forbes, also an old naval medical officer, and from all accounts he was a happy-go-lucky kind of person. His chief amusement was driving over all kinds of roads, often in danger of breaking his own neck and that of anyone who chose to ride with him.

Forbes would often go away for six weeks' holiday at a time, during which, he allowed people to take care of themselves. It was during one of these intervals that the Laird of Faskally prevailed on Dr Irvine (who had come to spend a holiday in his native place after graduation) to settle down and commence practice in Pitlochry. This was to bring a new style of medical practitioner to the Highlands of Perthshire. Prior to Dr Stewart and Dr Forbes, and later working alongside them, were old wise women who acted as midwives and nurses with knowledge of herbal remedies and many superstitions for cures.

In 1839, a statistical account for the Parish of Moulin (which included Pitlochry, Kinnaird, Auldclune, and Enochdhu) showed that the population was 2,039, not much different from today, but the difference was that then only about 600 lived in the village, while the other 1,400 lived in the landward areas, unlike today. Consequently, Dr Irvine had a tremendous amount of travelling and ground to cover to serve his patients the vast majority of whom were Gaelic speakers living in squalor. The bulk of the population of the parish lived in little 'black houses' with a fire in the middle of the one room – the smoke percolating through the heather thatch. Animals when brought in were kept in a stall at the end of the one room. It would not have been easy for Dr Irvine to see or to keep his equipment clean.

The only professional men living in the area were a lawyer, a banker, Dr Irvine, seven school teachers, and a minister. And yet, the Parish of Moulin was fortunate: a government inquiry in 1852, of 155 Highland parishes, found that only 62 had a doctor. (In Mull, there was no doctor until 1850, so if someone on Mull wanted to see a doctor, they had to travel to Inveraray.)

General Wade had built the old A9 and in Dr Irvine's time a stage-coach ran to Inverness, but the roads, where they existed, were in terrible condition. Each morning in Pitlochry, men would use a metal grid and drag this across the main thoroughfares levelling the surface – in summer raising huge clouds of dust, in winter flattening piles of mud and filling in ruts. In 1832, a bridge was built over the River Tummel and another was built over the River Garry at Killiecrankie in 1836. These eliminated some of the river crossings required when rivers rose in spate without warning or during winter flooding.

William Irvine was a man of average height and weight, keen, active, and quick-tempered. He had deep-set piercing grey eyes with shaggy eyebrows. He was the best of company: he could tell a good story and appreciate a good joke, at which he would laugh long and heartily. He could not stand cant nor humbug, and whatever he undertook, he went into with all his might. Dr Irvine had a lot of common sense and was a very good judge of human nature. He always spoke to the Highlanders in their native language, and held in contempt those people who, when going south, tried to forget their Gaelic.

Dr Irvine began his professional work possessed of all the medical knowledge his university could bestow on him. Even after 40 years of work, Dr Irvine remained a diligent student, acquiring the latest text-books and reading medical papers to keep himself abreast of the times and in touch with the leading men in his profession. Amongst his most intimate friends were Principal Edward Forbes, Dr Norman McLeod, Dr John Brown, Professor John Stuart Blackie, Miss Emma Molyneux, Miss Henrietta McInroy, Alexander Duff (when he was home from India) and many of the land owners of the area.

Dr Irvine lived in Craigatin, a house at the West End of Pitlochry after Dysart Cottages, and now a guest house. Craigatin had a large amount of stabling as in early days all Dr Irvine's visiting was done on horseback or by gig, covering large distances from Rannoch Moor in the west to Kirkmichael in the east; to Dalnaspidal in the north plus Ballinluig and surrounding districts in the south east. In the 1700s, 1800s, and early 1900s, these areas around Pitlochry were well populated with small hamlets and many black houses, as well as with houses provided for those who worked on the estates.

Dr Irvine's journeys visiting patients were done alone with only a lantern and his horse for company. Initially, Dr Irvine had difficulty in bringing the local community around to his abilities of curing or at least helping those in ill health. The fact that his father was the minister in Little Dunkeld and one of his father's brothers was the minister in Blair Athole may well have aided the populace to trust and believe in him. For word of mouth would have gone before him as he moved forward in his medical visits, keeping himself well informed by his contacts in the medical schools and their output in papers.

His many tasks would have included the lancing of abscesses, amputations (without anaesthetic) following compound fractures which could and probably would lead to sepsis, gangrene, and death. Midwifery was another problem for Dr Irvine who would only be called for complications in childbirth when maybe a mother's pelvis was too small, or a breach birth was involved. Additionally, he would have seen a lot of childhood deaths resulting from measles, diphtheria, scarlet fever, and whooping cough.

Dr Irvine would employ numerous herbal remedies made up in his dispensary: coltsfoot for asthma, black spleenwort (a fern) for tuberculosis, wild garlic for rheumatism, eyebright for eyes, foxglove for heart failure (today in its purified form, digitalis, or digoxin), and willow bark for fever or rheumatism (today in a purified form, aspirin).

To keep his dispensary stocked, regular visits to the hedgerows and fields of the district were necessary to find suitable plants. These were then dried and made into infusions at different strengths. At a later date, Dr Irvine employed a nineteen-year old apothecary, Robert Halliday from Moffat, Dumfriesshire, who remained with the doctor for most of their working lives (as well as Mercer Irving, aged 23).

At that time, opium was very important for the relief of pain and suffering; it has not been superseded to this day and is known as morphia in its refined form. Anyone could buy opium in its liquid form, then known as laudanum. Other treatments which were used frequently were hot poultices, cupping, and scarifiers. In Dr Irvine's day, there were many misconceived ideas about the body and the four humours, which, if they were out of balance, needed purging, vomits, and bleeding to get rid of excess.

Germs were unknown and infectious diseases were supposed to be due to a 'miasma' (a poisonous mist or vapour, supposedly having an evil or injurious effect). Dr Irvine, however, was well acknowledged for the lack of typhus and smallpox in his area, due to his ability to coax his patients to accept vaccinations for these ailments. Rheumatism and chest infections were common; rheumatism was not surprising due to heavy work and damp conditions.

By the 1850s, medicine and medical work were moving forward. Germs were discovered by Louis Pasteur, a French chemist and bacteriologist who developed pasteurisation; and Joseph Lister, a surgeon in Glasgow who realised the importance of hygiene, introduced carbolic sprays, and the cleaning of wounds with dilute carbolic. Work for Dr Irvine also eased slightly as chloroform was discovered in 1848, making operating a little easier.

Another medical role for Dr Irvine was that of surgeon to the Athole Highlanders and he was always present at the 'Athole Gathering'. He acted as its Secretary for many years and would often don the Highland dress and enjoy a good dance. On one occasion, he was chosen as one of four to dance a Highland reel before Queen Victoria at Blair Castle in 1844. The other three dancers were the Duke of Athole the Duke of Hamilton, and Charlie Christie, the Duke of Athole's personal attendant, who was also the trusted servant of the Dowager Duchess of Athole at Dunkeld House.

Dr Irvine's love of Pitlochry and the surrounding area kept him in his native hills so much that he could not leave. In his time, a great many changes had taken place thereabouts: the country population had gone down considerably, and the social conditions of the people had much improved. When Dr Irvine began his practice, typhus and scurvy were not uncommon, particularly during the short time after 1843, the year of the potato disease.

In addition to his medical duties, Dr Irvine was a Justice of the Peace for the County of Perth and an Elder in the Established Church. He was a keen politician and a Conservative all his life. On a lighter side of the doctor, he did regret that he could never persuade John Cameron, a Pitlochry weaver, to try the high jump at the 'Atholl Gathering'. John had earned a reputation as a jumper by a famous jump over two horses. Another acquaintance was a 'strapper' at Fisher's Hotel. He was a runner of the 'long-winded' type. It was no trouble for the strapper, after the mail coach had passed Carndearg (half-a-mile on its way to Moulinearn), to leave Fisher's Hotel with a forgotten parcel and overtake the Royal Mail coach. The strapper's historic feat was his enduring fame to be able to start from the front door of Fisher's Hotel and reach the summit of Ben-y-Vrackie within an hour – going by Baledmund and Craigvrack and topping the Ben in 58 minutes.

As Dr Irvine was known to keep his own chemist and dispensary, one day a country innkeeper came to the house and enquired of the doctor if he could give him anything for mixing with whisky. *"Yes"*, said the doctor, *"wait till I bring it"*. On his return, he held his riding whip. *"You villain"*, said he, *"I'll teach you to spoil good drink"*.

As a GP, Dr Irvine took a leading part in the preservation of social order. Coming out by his own gate one day, he noticed two tramps fighting. Hurrying towards them, he found the weaker one prostrate and the other continually kicking him. The doctor ordered the attacker to desist, and the man squared up to fight. At that time, the doctor was in his prime and in good fighting form. It only required the impudence of the tramp to raise his 'birze' (to put up a fight, raise his fists); with one blow on the chin, Dr Irvine levelled the tramp beside his bleeding chum. Still the impudent tramp rose up, but another leveller from the doctor sobered him. By this time, Dr Irvine's coachman appeared and was despatched for the police. Once the offender was safely in custody, Dr Irvine had the other carried into his house in order to dress his wounds.

It is regretted that of his vast experience both medical and social, Dr Irvine never put anything in writing and there is no doubt that many of the stories and traditions of the Highlands died with him, in particular the Highland history pertaining to the Jacobite Rising of 1745, for he must have heard of a great many incidents of that time from his mother who was one of the Stewarts of Garth and was intimately acquainted and had sympathy with many who took a leading part on the Jacobite side. Dr Irvine's mother was a descendant of the Wolf of Badenoch and his uncle, Major-General David Stewart of Garth, produced *Sketches of the Character, Institutions, and Customs of the Highlanders of Scotland* (1822) and a valuable history of the Black Watch and other Highland regiments and clans.

On 12th February 1850, at Balnakeilly, Pitlochry, Dr Irvine married Sarah Margaret Black. Sarah was born in Edinburgh in 1821, the fourth daughter of Henry Black of Mount Ulston, Jedburgh, Roxburghshire, a landed proprietor, and merchant. She was connected to the House of Balnakeilly by a half-sister of Henry Black's second wife. The couple produced five children.

JESSIE MARION STEWART IRVINE – Born 28th April 1851 in Pitlochry; married Frederick Preston Lees (1848-1918) in Pitlochry in 1874. They had seven children: two sons (one of whom was married with descendants) and five daughters (three married with descendants). Jessie died in London in 1936.

ALEXANDER (ALASTAIR) STEWART IRVINE – Born 23rd April 1852, died 1871.

HENRY STEWART IRVINE – Born 1854 in Pitlochry, married 23rd December 1894 in Edinburgh to Mary Ann Rattray (b. 1876) of Pitlochry. Henry died between 1930 and 1935.

MARGARET ELIZA STEWART IRVINE – Born 11th December 1859, died 1862.

WILLIAM STEWART IRVINE – Born 14th February 1861 in Pitlochry, married Emelie Louise Miller. They had two sons and a daughter, all of whom had descendants, mainly in Canada. William died in 1936.

It is interesting to note that there are distant relatives still living in Pitlochry: two whose grandfather was a nephew of Dr Irvine; and a third, whose mother was a cousin of that grandfather.

By 1891, after 58 years as a medical practitioner, Dr Irvine had witnessed many changes and developments both locally and nationally. The industrial revolution progressed taking away a lot of home industries and causing in some areas (the Highlands being one) more poverty and squalor. The cities too struggled. There was a lot of emigration to Canada, the USA, and Australia. Locally in Perthshire, this happened to a degree. Pitlochry, instead of being two small hamlets – East and West Pitlochry – and Moulin, the people in more outlying areas moved into villages and towns abandoning the distant 'black houses' on the hillsides. Dr Irvine may have found this reduced his journeying, but for air-borne diseases such as tuberculosis and smallpox the confined houses may have increased their spread. Dr Irvine too had seen both bad harvests and the poverty and the misery the death of an animal could cause when the ordinary man was already living with terrible conditions and destitute and could not afford a doctor.

Above and below: Pitlochry's main street in the 1870s.

Dr Irvine came in 1833 as a young man of 22 to a district which was primitive, isolated, and Gaelic speaking. He covered huge distances on horseback on poor roads and tracks, he administered to rich and poor alike, he was involved in much of his community's activities. His first assistant was a druggist and then his nephew Dr Robert Irvine. He kept himself well-informed and up-to-date, he married and had five children. His work was his life although he mixed extensively with local and visiting people, he encouraged everyone to learn and took a lively interest in the village reading room, an institution which was started in a small way by the Misses Butter of Faskally. It became the most successful of its kind in the country.

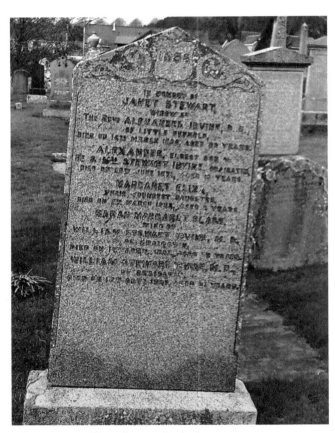

William Stewart Irvine's gravestone.

Sadly, on 1st April 1893 (at 11.25 pm), his wife Sarah died aged 72 of gastroenteritis after suffering for two months; exhaustion eventually brought her end. Later the same year (14th October), Dr William Stewart Irvine died (at 2.20 am) of gastritis which he had suffered from for three months, plus mitral disease of the heart and exhaustion; Dr Irvine was 81 years of age.

At this point it seems appropriate to allow Emma Molyneux who knew Dr Irvine himself to elucidate on the man.

In the autumn of 1893 there was an October day which will long be remembered in Pitlochry, for into that day both summer and autumn seemed to have poured their fullest splendour, so that the land was lit up as if from some hidden source of glory. The woods had on their richest colouring – one might almost say there was a sunset glow in every tree, – and the air was soft and sun-laden.

This was the day of Dr Irvine's funeral, and even as it was the perfection and consummation of a matchless summer, so in the long procession that wound along the vale and up the hill to Moulin churchyard, there were representatives of all that was noblest and most characteristic in the district where his beneficent life was lived. The Duke of Atholl with his two sons and his Highlanders walked there, followed by friends of every class and station of life, from far and near. The coffin, wrapped in a plaid, was reverently carried by true mourners, while the pipes wailed out the strains of regret and hope – 'Lochaber no More', and 'The Land o' the Leal'.

Thus was the last outward honour paid to William Stewart Irvine, and the place that knew him so long knows him now no more; but as 'the memory of the just is blessed', so the tradition of his noble life, in all its simplicity and reality, will go down the stream of time beyond our seeing or hearing. It is good to recall him now as he was, to brace ourselves for the way that remains by the thought of his true and manful spirit, which endured to the end and won the crown of a faithful life.

But to speak of him with full knowledge and power should be the work of others; the present recollections are only, as it were, a wreath laid on his grave in the name of friendship and gratitude.

In former days, no one could be long in the Vale of Athole without hearing the name of Dr Irvine as a household word; and thus it was that some time before actually meeting him I seemed to know the 'Old Doctor', as he was as he was affectionately called. The Doctor's word was, in those days, as a law to the country-people, his advice authoritative, his voucher a complete character in itself. *"The Doctor knows me well"* was often the one and only testimonial thought necessary on either side. And well might it be so, for fifty years of family histories came within his own personal experience, and behind them lay a great store of inherited knowledge and tradition. He stood, as it were, at the parting of the ways between the old clannish life of the Highlands, full of individuality and local colouring, of wild poetry and loyal, long-cherished devotions, and the new order of things advancing slowly, steadily, like a rising flood that submerges old landmarks, obliterates old traces, and levels old barriers, until those who knew the land from childhood would wander as strangers through it. So is the old order passing away, year by year, in the Highlands, though the change may be stayed here and there by special efforts or conditions. But in Dr Irvine's keen, retentive memory one could read as in a mirror the life of days gone by for ever, could trace the origin and growth of lingering customs, the meaning of certain characteristics – in fact, could share in hopes and fears that are now no more than survivals, could, as has been well said, 'behold the series of the generations' and 'weigh with surprise the momentous and nugatory gift of life'. Yes; and he himself, was he not the embodiment of much that is found nowhere but in these Highlands? Was he not the life of their life, in the best sense?

Shrewd, sagacious, hardy and enduring, faithful and laborious, with a fire of enthusiasm, a vein of the unconscious poetry that ran glancing through all his talk, and made every word of it interesting. Never have I heard from him a commonplace or colourless remark; whatever might be the subject, it suggested to his mind an experience, an anecdote, an illustration touched with humour and pathos, and, best of all, drawn from life. No second-hand talk, no borrowed opinions, no thought of effect, but just the outpouring of a sagacious, sympathetic mind, stored with facts of human life. The many distinguished men he had known, either professionally or otherwise, were brought before you by a few graphic touches, some salient trait given that told more than a page of generalities, and there was the man before you whom Dr Irvine had known and whom you henceforth knew. It is wonderful to see how people and events live on in such a mind as his.

But what avails description of a real character like Dr Irvine? How can I show the man himself who was the soul of all he said? No more than I can picture for others the rugged, benevolent face, strong, square-browed, bearing the impress of thought and power; the deep-set grey eyes that could gleam with humour and glow with enthusiasm; the rare, genial, sympathetic smile straight from the heart; all, in fact, that blended in his aspect the strong and the lovable.

Dr Irvine's descent, on the mother's side, was from an old Highland family, the Stewarts of Garth, and in face he bore a strong resemblance to his famous uncle, General Stewart of Garth, author of *Sketches of the Highlands,* etc. etc. The ruined stronghold of the family still stands at the head of the Keltney Burn, some way from Aberfeldy, a grey, massive keep, isolated and impressive even in its decay. Dr Irvine was also linked with the most romantic episode of Scottish history through his great-grandfather, Mr. Stewart of Kynachan, who followed Prince Charlie, and was imprisoned at Carlisle for his share in the uprising. I have heard Dr Irvine relate how some friends managed to convey relief to the captive by sending a large snuff-box full of snuff, but so remarkably weighty that his great-grandfather, on investigation found at the bottom of it golden guineas with which he bribed his gaoler to loosen his chains so far as to allow of his lying down! He was subsequently released, and returned home with a new acquisition in a 'viol de gamba', which he had learnt to play in prison. The portrait of this ancestor hung in the dining-room at Craigatin (the house which Dr Irvine built for himself at Pitlochry), along with a fine Raeburn of his grandfather and other interesting portraits, and one could not but feel in intercourse with him that he had inherited, not merely the memories, but much of the innermost life of a remarkable race. Besides his strong and distinctively Scottish qualities, there were in him ideals that came from an age more poetic than ours. The old world courtesy, so unfailing, the self-devotion to a cause, regardless of consequences (in his case the cause was the claims of his profession taken in the noblest sense), the loyalty to all who trusted him, the fatherly care for all who depended on him, the fine enthusiasm for principles and disregard of personal advancement, these attributes, which ought to be among the plainest signs of good descent, were the great attractions of his character. 'Spirits are not finely touched but to fine issues', and the influence of any such man during a long life of work can never be estimated, but it is not often that circumstances combine, as in this case, to develop the utmost resources of a rich nature.

When Dr Irvine first came to Pitlochry in 1833 the district was comparatively unknown and unvisited. Communication was slow and difficult in the absence of a railway or of roads like the present splendid highway. His responsibility as parish doctor extended over forty-five miles of country, much of it wild moorland only to be reached by rough, precipitous roads, almost impassable for weeks at a time in winter. This wide district he had to traverse on horseback, and often far beyond its bounds he was called for private practice or consultation. Single-handed he had to struggle with difficulties that would have dismayed a far stronger man than he was physically, but which in time only served to develop that high courage which is the groundwork of every virtue, the backbone of every principle. Little or no professional help was to be had, and often, in the early years of his practice, he was summoned to some distant farm or croft to fight a disease he had perhaps had no previous opportunity of studying. There, in the wilds, far from all resources, he had to rely on his own penetration and sagacity, with no efficient nursing, nothing on his side in the battle save the calm endurance of the children of toil and their faith in him. In a case of this kind he would leave minute directions for the nursing during the following day or two, foreseeing every contingency and knowing the impossibility of returning earlier; then would ride home, without rest maybe, to find an urgent summons in another direction. Utterly exhausted, he would perhaps fling himself down on the hearthrug for an hour or two of rest, then take a light meal and start off for another long ride. At such times he was hardly seen by his own family for days together. After some years, when he had prevailed upon other doctors to settle down at different points of this extensive district, things became easier, but a life of continuous and unremitting toil was his until threescore and ten had been reached and passed.

Imagine the power for good of a man of this stamp in his daily familiar intercourse with the people. Speaking their own Gaelic, familiar with their ways of thinking, he was trusted as few are ever trusted in this world, and this nobly earned trust enabled him to render services quite apart from his profession. He knew the daily lives, the needs, the hopes and fears of the people as if they had all been of his own family; he was the trusted friend, the helper in need of all who sought his aid.

Dr William Stewart Irvine in later life.

When he first began work in it, the country was still under the influence of old ideals and memories, still ignorant of King Demos and all his ways. *Poor* the people were, deplorably 'narrow', no doubt (according to modern notions), and wanting in the most elementary ideas of creature comfort, but in the main independent, reverent, holding fast by antiquated beliefs in righteous retribution and reward, and having a certain originality which is the portion of those who think their own thoughts and are in daily contact with the powers of Nature. The *few* books they possessed were really mastered; the art of conversation was valued and practised in a way that would shame some of the 'highest circles', and in every glen was to be found some one with a retentive memory to hand down the legends and songs and ballads of far-gone days. Gifts of song or story-telling were highly valued at the 'Ceilidh', or friendly gathering of several families round one fireside during the long winter evenings, when the women brought their knitting, and spinning-wheels, the men busied themselves with creel-making and other handiwork, while first one and then another kept up the 'flow of soul' by music or recitation.

From Dr Irvine's strong, vivid memory and his picturesque phraseology what a book of reminiscences might have been produced! But he never could find time to write down any notes during his busy life, and when the leisure came with advancing years, he was too tired! Speaking one day of the changes that had gradually come about in the country within his own recollection, he gave the following facts: 'My recollections', he said, 'are of the primitive times, which were times of starvation. I remember, at a certain meeting of the Turnpike Trustees, there were two old men present, one a guest, the other a treasurer of the Trust. The former mentioned that in bringing up meal for the supply of the country (before 1816) only one boll of meal could be carried at a time in a cart because of the badness of the roads. The other man said, "If your memory had carried you further back, you'd have remembered when *no* cart could come up; when one man led a horse or pony which had six or eight others tied together behind each with a sack of meal on his back, and only thus could they get the meal up into the country". The population was too large for the produce of the country. When I came here in 1833 the population of Moulin parish was 2,300; now, in 1891, it is about 2,000, notwithstanding the growth of Pitlochry. The meal always ran done before the end of the season while the people were at the shielings. The time spent at the shielings was between sowing their crop (in May) until they returned to reap late in autumn. An old woman in my time remembered that there was often only enough meal remaining to take to the shieling to feed the baby of the house, and the others fed on salt meat and kippered salmon (so abundant in the rivers, which were not

16

preserved) and milk; the milk kept them from dying of scurvy. Potatoes were not then largely used, in fact were scarcely known. Near the end of the last century they began to grow potatoes, and from that time food was more abundant, and the ravages of scurvy were stayed.

'The people were very active, but not very powerful; they have become, in my observation, a finer race physically, but I don't think more talented. I don't think the mixing with the Saxon has improved their intellect, but it has improved them in two ways: First, in regard to bodily size and strength; second, the Saxon prudence has controlled the Celtic impetuosity. Want of steadiness of purpose characterises the Celt ... I have known so many young fellows who got on well, and showed marked ability in a certain line; but then made a dash at something they did not know, failed, lost heart, and were ruined.'

Dr Irvine here alludes to the native cleverness of the Highlanders, and he used to tell many stories illustrative of their ingenuity and imagination. For instance, the story of a ghillie on one of the Perthshire shootings who was very enthusiastic about the Jacobite rising, and whose forefathers had taken an active part in it. He was being badgered by the 'Sassenach' shooting tenants, and had endured hearing the campaign and all who took part in it held up to ridicule for some time. At last he said quietly to one of the gentlemen who were standing on a piece of rising ground, 'Would you be so kind, sir, as to step down from that knowe?' 'Why?' was the query; 'what do you mean? 'I think, sir, it will be best if you will be stepping down from that knowe, for it is a very dangerous place; people will not be able to speak the truth while they are standing there'. That certainly was the retort courteous!

Many a man, finding himself so much isolated as Dr Irvine was in the early days of his practice, would have sunk down into a mere jog-trot existence, and never been heard of beyond the bounds of his own district. He, on the contrary, kept pace with the times by systematic reading, and kept in touch with the great world through his warm friendships. Pitlochry, though comparatively unknown as a health resort forty *of* fifty years ago, was yet frequented by some select spirits, men of science or of power in some line who resorted to it for summer quarters. In this way Dr Irvine became acquainted with some of his warmest friends. Among them were Dr John Brown, Principal Forbes,

Norman Macleod, and many others long since passed away: friends who, afforded him the stimulus of a society of pure, intellect and heart, of plain living and high thinking such as mere outward prosperity and so-called 'advantages' cannot always command. The reputation of his skill as a doctor induced many invalids to adventure themselves thus far in the Highlands, and by degrees the value of Pitlochry air, and the charms of its surroundings, became generally known. Few perhaps realise how much of the present prosperity of the place is due to the steadfast labours and high personal attainments of one man, and herein is the saying true – 'One soweth and another reapeth'. His unaffected simplicity and naturalness of character prevented him from estimating or understanding the extent of his power and influence, and in fact, from his own point of view, his life was chiefly remarkable for the kindness and goodness of his numerous friends, and the many blessings bestowed on him by Heaven. He took little account of the lives saved and the homes blessed *by* his skill and sympathy.

Dr Irvine was the son of a Highland minister well known in his day, and a brother of the still well-remembered Dr Irvine, minister of Blair-Athole. He was himself a devoted adherent of the Church of Scotland, and, in his last years, when released from pressing professional claims, he became an elder, in order, as he said, 'to be still of some little use'. Many will long remember the frail, venerable form, Sunday by Sunday, passing down the Parish Church with the collecting-bag, and will recall the kindly gleam that shot from time to time from his eyes, softened by time and trouble.

And now that he has passed away from the place that knew him so long, it seems to have lost its animating and unifying spirit, and to be resolved into more prosaic elements. But he was weary, and longed for rest. His work was done, and, to such a man, what is life without work? – a lingering death! The last few years of his life had been marked by severe trials, and in the early part of 1893 came the death of his wife, which left him for the first time face to face with loneliness. This supreme trial he met with Christian fortitude and resignation, but his strength and life ebbed gradually away, and to 'depart in peace' became thenceforth his one desire and prayer. *Home* for him meant no longer his beloved Vale of Athole, nor even the well-known house by the banks of the Tummel, but the Father's house of many mansions – the 'Land o' the Leal'.

[Emma Molyneux, *Recollections of William Stewart Irvine MD., FRCSE* (Edinburgh: David Douglas, 1896).]

CHAPTER TWO

Dr Robert William Irvine – 'Dr Bob'

O N 19TH APRIL 1853, Robert William Irvine was born in Blair Athole. He was baptised in Blair Athole on 31st October 1853. Irvine was the youngest of five children from his father's second marriage, so Dr Bob – he was known locally as 'Dr Bob' to distinguish him from his uncle who was known as 'The Old Doctor' – had a half-sister, Elizabeth McKenzie Stewart Menzies Irvine. Dr Bob's father was Alexander Robertson Irvine, the minister in Blair Athole and the brother of Dr William Irvine. His mother was Sophia Stewart Robertson of Kindrochet.

Alexander Robertson Irvine was born in Fortingall on 30th January 1806 and was also a minister of Foss from 1830-42, Fortingall 1842-3, and Blair Athole 1843-67. He married Sophia Jane Stewart Robertson (*c.*1818-1856).

Dr Bob's grandparents on his father's side were Alexander Irvine who was born in Fortingall, 1st November 1773. He married Janet (Jessie) Stewart who was born 3rd April 1776 on 3rd April 1805. Jessie died 18th March 1865 at Lagreach, Pitlochry. Alexander died in Little Dunkeld on 31st July 1824, where he had been the minister from 1806-24. Dr Bob had four siblings.

SOPHIA STEWART ROBERTSON IRVINE Born 1845, married John Robertson 1867, with whom she had four sons. She died in 1910.

ALEXANDER ROBERTSON IRVINE ROBERTSON – Born 30th April 1847, who on reaching 21 and succeeding to his mother's property of Kindrochet, added his mother's surname to his own. He married Emily Cook who was born 6th January 1848 and died 30th April 1900. They had six children.

CLEMENTINA IRVINE – Born in 1849 in Blair Athole and married Charles Winchester (who served in the Indian Civil Service) in 1875. There is no known issue.

DUNCAN ROBERTSON IRVINE – Born 1851 in Blair Athole, baptised in Blair Athole on 14th May 1851, married Sarah White. There is no known issue. He died in Victoria, British Columbia on 17th March 1914, and is buried in Ross Bay cemetery.

Robert Willliam Irvine.

Dr Bob was educated first at Madras College St Andrews, then Edinburgh Academy, entering Edinburgh University at the age of sixteen, and gaining the degrees MA (1872), MB, CM, and FRCSE (1880).

He joined his uncle Dr William Irvine in his Pitlochry practice in 1876, at the age of 23. All these accomplishments he achieved while still maintaining his strong interest in all sporting activities and also taking an interest in public matters – in politics he was a strong Conservative. Dr Bob was gifted with high mental attainments and, with a ready flow of language, was a graphic and forcible speaker.

Rosehill, Pitlochry.

According to the 1891 *Census of Pitlochry*, Dr Bob and his wife lived in Rosehill at the east end of Pitlochry next to where the Hydro Electric shop used to be. Dr Bob's wife Wilhelmina (Minnie) Hogg, who he married on 27th January 1887 in Forteviot, was born 21st August 1861 in Culross, Perthshire, which is now part of Fife. When they married, the couple were in their thirties and there is no knowledge of any issue. Wilhelmina's father was the factor for Lord Elgin's Valleyfield Estate. She was one of five daughters. There is no further information about her.

Dr Bob's keen interest in sporting activities at school and university was widely known and there have been few, if any, better exponents of the game of rugby. When in 1871, Edinburgh Academical Football Club (Edinburgh Accies) staged the world's first rugby international at Raeburn Place, Edinburgh (the Murrayfield ground did not open until 1925), there were six Accies players in the side, including the skipper, the Honorary Francis Moncrieff, and two legends of the early game, Robert 'Bulldog' Irvine and James Finlay. 'Bulldog' Irvine was of course Dr Bob who was given the appellation of 'The Bulldog'; a term peculiarly expressive of the tenacity with which he would stick to the ball in his possession. Dr Bob gained his first England-Scotland Rugby International in that match, playing of course for Scotland which was victorious over England.

Scotland beat England at Raeburn Place, 1871.

Dr Bob was an original member of the committee which formed the Scotch Rugby Union. Dr Bob represented Scotland against England for ten successive years, being capped every year from 1871-1880 (inclusive). He captained the team on five occasions, and also played for Scotland against Ireland from 1877-1880.[1] From Dr Bob's first cap, received when only seventeen years old in the inaugural international, to his last cap (his thirteenth), he was exceptionally strong, athletic, and devastating when tackling and skilful at dribbling, with clever line-out work, which along with leadership skills made him an exceptional person.

Dr Bob later gained medals for stone and hammer throwing at the Athole gatherings, where he competed against professionals. For some years, he was a member of the Academicals Cricket XI and participated in Edinburgh University boxing and golf competitions. He also won the Athole Cross of Perth Royal Golfing Society. As a patron of Vale of Athole Football Club, he had a large involvement in the provision of the recreation ground and golf course facilities in Pitlochry. Dr Bob's life was very full: apart from his medical work he was an officer in the Athole Highlanders, an enthusiastic Free Mason, as well as a Forester.

In 1876, when Dr Bob joined his uncle in his practice, the patients'

---

1   There were no matches with Wales in those days.

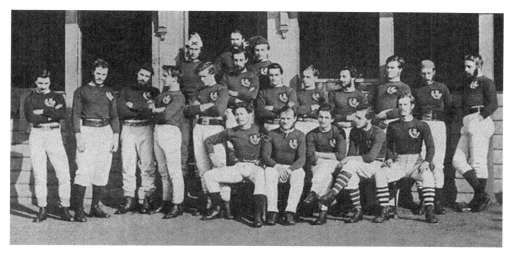

Scotland's International Rugby Team, 1871.
Robert 'Bulldog' Irvine stands 5th from the left in the middle row.

area covered Tulliemet, Ballinluig, Pitlochry, Moulin, Enochdhu, Blair Athole and the whole area to the county march. Transport was mainly by horse or horse and gig, but the railway was appearing and could be used if needed, but within limits.

Dr Bob's life as a doctor could not have been easy, but he was remembered as an extremely good doctor. Although sometimes thought to be a bit rough, his cheeriness, his good Gaelic, and his ability to get on with everybody no matter their status made him popular. It was, however, in surgery that his real skill lay, and many people owed him their lives following operations carried out with the simplest of equipment on scrubbed kitchen tables. Here is a case in point.

A Case of a Gunshot Wound of the Head

By Robert Wm. Irvine, MA, MB, CM, FRCSE, Etc. Pitlochry

A case of surgical and medico-interest, in which a gunshot glancing wound of the head, involving considerable loss of brain tissue and considerable loss of skull, recovered. The healed wound was photographed, and places on record an authentic proof of the shape which a healed gunshot wound, delivered within a limit of from 6 to 10 feet from muzzle to object, would present; of interest, especially in view of the importance of its shape, in reference to the direction from which the shot was fired.

W. D. aged about 13, a herd boy, was inadvertently shot in the head on 20th of September, 1881. The shot was from a single-barrelled old-fashioned gun, percussion action, loaded with No. 6 and 5 lead drops, and ordinary black powder, muzzle-loading. The accident occurred in a farmyard, whose dimensions enable me to bring the range as not more than 10 feet, and not likely less than 6 feet, though possibly as short as 4 feet. The injured lad had on a cloth cap. He was shot 'from in front', in the left frontal parietal region. Bonnet and skull debris, with cerebral slush, were deeply in the brain wound, and had to be hooked out by the fingers from as deep as the region of the base. The sensation was, that so deep was the finger that a rash dig for debris might touch too hard a vital centre, and startle one with a catastrophe. But luckily that did not occur. The boy fell to the shot, but was not unconscious; and, wounded as he was, made at least 10 yards of his way to the house before he sank and required help.

The wound was rendered as aseptic as possible, and manual pressure uninterruptedly kept up, with an ice-cap, from the first, to counteract the inevitable tendency to 'hernia cerebri', but of no avail. By the end of two weeks a cerebral protrusion of not less than 2 inches of cauliflower brain excrescence was there, and always on the increase. The orthodox thing was to shave it off, and keep doing it as it protruded. I had already been so near the base of the brain, that I avoided that ex cathedra method of dealing, and adopted another, and, I believe, the wise course – I starved the boy, and kept him in a sitting posture continuously, with the manual ice-pressure, never intermitted; gave him ice-water and milk, and large doses of bromide of potassium. Within seven days of this my hopes began to be realized. The protruding, wagging cauliflower had got smaller. The line of ulceration between its base and the bone margin had given way to a pronounced development of the blue line of cicatrization; the union of the internal and external once established, 'hey presto!' like magic the hernia cerebri was pulled back into its cage, and the wound healed in another week. And from start to finish there was never a bad symptom referable to the brain injury, except an irritable alteration in his temperament, and a very marked, very interesting, and very instructive want of word memory – 'amnesia aphasia'. The boy has since then, except for the temporary discomfort of the irritation caused by the separation of the spicular fragments from the margins of the fossa, never had a bad turn, and has for over ten years been doing ordinary work as a wood forester in the Duke of Atholl's estate service.

The illustration is from a photograph taken, as I have said, in my presence whenever the wound was healed. The shot was from in front. The white mark represents a fontanelle, 2½ inches by 1¼ inches broad at its base at the back; and all the white portion representing cicatrix – no bone – and pulsating, the apex of the triangle being the glancing bone wound of impact, the square base the deepest bone wound, and quite abrupt. The boy is quite well, except that he has a certain excitability and want of inhibitory power when provoked.

I offer you this narrative because I think it has an inherent surgical interest of its own; and also because, with the authentic illustration, it has bearing, in my humble opinion, more cogent, and more proved, than any evidence regarding gunshot wounds and their probable direction and shape adduced at the late Ardlamont trial, – a trial in which every medical man in this country, especially if he can handle a gun, and has some shooting, must have, and as a matter of fact has, taken a deep and cogent interest.

Printed by Adam Doggat [sic] & Co., Pitlochry.

[Reprinted from the *Edinburgh Medical Journal*
for April 1894 by kind permission.]

Following his retirement from rugby internationals in 1880, Dr Bob was still busy with his work and local activities. Along with his team, he won the Duchess of Athole's 'Broom' for curling (a very coveted trophy among curlers in Athole). He also enjoyed shooting and fishing, but somehow, even with all his activities and interests, he had trouble with his weight and had difficulties with obesity; rumour also put it forward that he had an alcohol problem. Sadly, on 18th April 1897, Dr Bob died, due it was thought to a contusion of the hip and traumatic delirium. He was 46 years old. His funeral was well attended and a solemn occasion.

On Wednesday the remains of the late Dr R.W. Irvine were laid to rest within the New Cemetery at Dysart, Pitlochry. The obsequies were public, and while the interment was taking place the shops and public offices in Pitlochry were closed and the blinds of private homes were drawn. Evidence of the respect in which deceased was held was observed in the large and representative attendance of mourners, of whom upwards of 1,000 were present, the funeral being the largest that has been seen in the district. There was a large representation of the members of Lodge St Andrew (No. 814, Pitlochry) of Freemasons, and there was a deputation present from Lodge St John (No. 14, Dunkeld). An apology for absence was received front Colonel Graham Stirling of Strowan, Depute Provincial Grand Master. There, was also a large turn-out of the members of Court Vale of Atholl (No. 6707) A.O.F., together with representatives of the Pitlochry Curling Club, the members of the various Societies being attired in the uniform of their respective organisations. A short service was con ducted by Rev. James Fraser, Blair Atholl, and Rev. D. M. Donald, B.D., Moulin. Thereafter a procession was formed in the following order- Pipers, Freemasons, curlers, coffin, relatives, Foresters, general public. The coffin was of polished-oak with brass mountings, and bore the following inscription on the lid – "Robert W. Irvine, M. B. Born 19th April 1853; died 18th April 1897". The coffin was carried successively by relays of Freemasons, curlers, Foresters, and the public. The cortège proceeded slowly through the village to the solemn strains of 'The Land o' the Leal'. The streets were lined with sympathetic spectators, on whom the spectacle produced a profound impression. The concluding portion of the service was performed at the grave by the Rev. Andrew Meldrum, Logierait. Thereafter the remains were committed to the dust, the pall-bearers being Rev. Robertson Irvine, Clackmannan, (brother); Mr T. Richmond; Mr J. Robertson, jun., Old Blair; Mr W. Robertson; and Mr Alister Fraser, Findrack (nephews); Mr John Robertson, Old Blair (brother-in-law); Mr Hugh Mitchell, Pitlochry; Mr Henry Fergusson, Pitlochry. The grave was beautifully lined with evergreens and a profusion of primroses, the late doctor's birthday having been on Primrose Day. After the coffin had been lowered into the ground the usual Masonic rites were gone through. The senders of wreaths included the senior boys of Pitlochry School; and the Vale of Atholl Football Club.

[*Dundee Courier*, 22 April 1897]

In September of the following year, a memorial was raised in honour of Dr Bob.

A monument to the memory of Dr Robert Irvine, Pitlochry, who died amid great expressions of regret in the district in April last year, was unveiled in Pitlochry in Pitlochry Cemetery yesterday.

Many tributes have been paid to Dr Irvine's qualities as a man and as a professional gentle man and these have now found material expression in the chaste and handsome monument unveiled yesterday.

The opportunity of contributing towards the perpetuation of so worthy a memory was cordially embraced by his friends and neighbours in Pitlochry district, as well as by his college chums and comrades in the athletic field, where he in his younger days took so notable place. The result was the accumulation of funds sufficient to procure a

Robert Irvine's grave, Dysart Cemetery, Pitlochry.

memorial alike worthy of the doctor's memory and of the high place he held in the affections and respect of the people. The commission for the execution of the memorial was placed in the hands of Messrs Scott& Rae, Glasgow. The monument takes the form of a Celtic cross standing over thirteen feet high. It is silver-grey Kirkcudbrightshire granite, and stands on a triple base. On the face of the cross are carved sculptures of the style of Scotland symbolic chiefly of the idea of eternity. The inscription appears of the upper and middle base and is as follows: – Erected in memory of Robert William Irvine, M.A, M.B, C.M, FRCSE., Pitlochry.

Born 19th April 1863, died 18th April 1897. By a large circle of his friends in admiration of his rare professional skills, his great mental gifts, his eloquence, and his wide and varied knowledge: in recognition of his distinction as a manly exponent of our national athletic recreations, and in loving testimony to his kindness of heart and his ever ready and helpful sympathy with the poor of the district. Aig Fois". There is also a border to the grave of the same granite material as the monument.

The huge crowd which yesterday witnessed the unveiling by Mr Hugh Mitchell was ample testimony, if such were needed, of the great hold which the memory of Dr Irvine's personality retains on the people of the district. The proceedings were initiated by a procession from the Parish Church, passing along Pitlochry main street, to the west of which lies the secluded cemetery. The procession was headed by six pipers (two of them the Duke of Atholl's from the Atholl Highlanders). These were Corporal A. Stewart and Thos. McLachlan and the others were Messrs A. Gordon, Mitchell Pirnie, Duncan Campbell and Robert Meikle. Following the pipers, who played a lament throughout the short route, came the Court Vale of Atholl Ancient Order of Foresters, the members wearing the regalia and the Court banner borne aloft.

Mr Mitchell drew aside the plaid covering the memorial. In doing so he said – Friends – for we are joined by the bonds of a common sorrow and the ties of a common sympathy – we are met today to commemorate one who, for fully more than twenty years, was the best known figure and perhaps the most prominent person in the Vale of Atholl, one who had a deeper hold on the hearts and affection of the people than anyone else is likely to have in our day and generation. Dr Robert Irvine was no ordinary man. He was endowed with great physical strength, and with equally great mental power. He was nobly equipped for the battle of life, and he was fitted in many respects to be a leader of men.

In his day he was recognised as one of the foremost athletes in Scotland and he particularly excelled in those national athletic recreations which are particular to the Highlands of Scotland. While on the football field he made a reputation, and has left a name which has endured to the present time, and is familiar to all lovers of the game. Mentally Dr Irvine had few superiors. His mind was at once original and powerful, his intellect had been carefully trained by a course of systematic study, added to which he had the gift of a most retentive memory, and once he had mastered a subject he never forgot it, while there were few subjects with which he was not familiar. He took none of his ideas second-hand. He thought out his opinions for himself and any subject – even his most hackneyed – acquired new interest when it was illuminated by the light of Dr Irvine's genius.

We all knew his charms as a conversationalist – he could adapt himself to every person and every company, and he had the gift of not only conveying his own ideas to others, but drawing out the best parts of men when they were in conversation with him. His eloquence was by no means confined to the limits of this district. He had not only the power of expressing his ideas in appropriate words, but he had a sort of intuitive power of gauging the feelings of the audience and of putting in graphic language the feelings and wishes of the moment. He was a true orator in every sense of the term, because most of us will admit that his brilliant speeches were made without any previous preparation, and on the spur of the moment. There was one gift, however, in which Dr Irvine per-eminently excelled. I may describe it as the gift of tactful sympathy. He could identify himself with the hopes and wishes and even the very life of the person who appealed to him for sympathy. Nor was this, by any means confined to those in his own class and station. The poorest cottager: nay, even the beggar by the dykeside, was just as sure of his sympathy as the richest person in the land. Nor can it be wondered, then, when Dr Irvine came here some twenty-one years ago in the full vigour of his youth and mental power, and trained with great professional skill and knowledge, that in a short time he won the hearts and sympathies of every person in the district, and well deserved it. I think that no finer type of a country doctor could be found than Dr Irvine at his best. In his profession he knew no distinction of rank. Everyone received the same care and attention. The rank was but the guinea stamp, and the poor person was quite as sure that they would receive just as much care as the richest. To the appeal of the poor and needy Dr Irvine never turned a deaf ear, and his purse was always open. No doubt his generosity was often abused, but many of the lapsed and fallen were encouraged to begin the battle of life afresh by the thought that Dr Irvine still believed in them. And had he not a great reward? Who in this district was ever more loved, who was welcomed in every house, and what is there that the people would not have done for beloved Dr Bob, as they all preferred to call him. We have to lament that perhaps Dr Irvine did not fully recognise the grand career that was before him, and that the latter part of his life was darkened by an ever deepening shadow. But his weaknesses and faults, such as they were, are but the inheritance of frail humanity. They are buried in the dust. We have long ago forgiven them, and while his virtues and noble qualities will remain ever treasured in our hearts. Nor do I think that the great Judge of all the earth will mete out to him and harder measure. It is too often our sad lot to lay in earth.

Life's glory dead,
Yet from the ground these blossoms red
Life that shall endless be.

And surely it is a comforting thought to think that the friendships of earth, freed from all earthly stain and passion, will be renewed, and broadened and deepened in the realms above, and that when our time comes to cross that wide and shadowy river that the first to give us joyous greeting on its further shore will be those to whom we were united on earth by ties of friendship and love. I now unveil this monument in token of our love and friendship of Dr Irvine, and in recognition of his many great and noble qualities, and in our belief in the efficacy of the cross of Christ, and in the sure and certain hope of a glorious immortality.

Rev Mr Irvine Robertson said he wished, on behalf of Mrs Irvine and the other relatives of his brother, the late Dr Irvine, to express most cordial thanks for that token of the esteem and affection in which his brother spent in Pitlochry represented a very large amount of earnest, arduous, and valuable service, not only in the medical profession, but in every other field of exertion wherein he could contribute to the well-being of that community. The monument was a memorial of those twenty years, and also a memorial of the wisdom, enlightenment, and good feeling of the men of Atholl and of a large community beyond.

Mt Mitchell expressed to the sculptors the general sense of satisfaction with the manner in which they had executed the work entrusted to them.

This closed the proceedings, the precession returning to the village again headed by the pipers.

[*Dundee Courier*, 27 September 1898]

EDINBURGH ACADEMICAL FOOTBALL CLUB
OTHER NOTES OF INTEREST

The game came to Edinburgh Academy in 1854 when two brothers from the City of Durham – Francis and Alexander Crombie – moved to Edinburgh. Both knew the rules, and when Francis enrolled at the Academy, he passed on his knowledge of the game which quickly took hold.

Founded in 1857-8, Edinburgh Academical Football Club is the oldest rugby club in Scotland, and second oldest in the world – the first being Trinity College, Dublin.

The club omits the word 'rugby' because its founding pre-dates the division between the Association and Rugby codes of football which took place in 1863.

The club has supplied two out of three of Scotland's Grand Slam captains (as of 2018): G. P. S. Macpherson in 1925 and David Sole in 1990.

Edinburgh Accies joined the Rugby Football Union in 1872 before resigning in 1873 to become one of the eight founder members of the organisation that later became the Scottish Rugby Union.

Since 1871 (as of 2018), a further 90 Accies have worn Scotland colours (five for England). In all, Accies claim that 96 Scotland players have come from the club, making it the most prolific suppliers of Scotland caps of any club north of the Border (only London Scottish have supplied more).

CENSUS INFORMATION
ABOUT THE RESIDENTS AT CRAIGATIN

1861
William Stewart Irvine – Head of Household, aged 48
Sarah Irvine – Spouse, aged 40
Jessie M. Irvine – Daughter, aged 10
Alexander M. Irvine – Son, aged 9
Henry Irvine – Son, aged 6
Margaret Eliza Irvine – Daughter, aged 2
William Irvine – Son, aged 1 month

1871
William Stewart Irvine
Sarah Irvine
Jessie M. Irvine
Alexander M. Irvine
William Irvine
Patrick Wall – Medical Student, aged 27

1881

William Stewart Irvine

Sarah Irvine

Henry F. Mudie – Medical Student, aged 30 (born Dundee)

Robert Halliday – Druggist, aged 19 (born Moffat)

James Cameron – Groom, aged 16 (born Blair Atholle)

John McLauchlan – Message Boy, aged 13 (born Blair Atholle)

Ann Stewart – Housemaid, aged 28 (born Blair Atholle)

Elizabeth Reid – Cook, aged 22 (born Moulin)

Helen R. Y. Barker – Housemaid, aged 20 (born Perth)

1891

William Stewart Irvine

Sarah Irvine

Fred Irvine Lees – Grandson, aged 16 (born Cheshire)

Samuel Beatty – Visitor (GP), aged 31 (born Abogill, Antrim)

That same year, Jessie M. S. Lees (*née* Irvine) resided in Station Road, Cheadle, Cheshire along with her husband Frederic P. Lees, two sons and a daughter, and two servants.

CHAPTER THREE

Henrietta Caroline McInroy – 13 June 1828 to 15 January 1898

H ENRIETTA CAROLINE McINROY was born in Renfrew. There is no known explanation for this as her parents by this time were either living or based in Lude, Blair Athole. Her family were engaged in businesses concerned with sugar, rum, and the slave trade in the West Indies.

Lude House, Blair Atholl.

As with many non-employed ladies of that time, of those who remained single, little or nothing is known. With some exceptions, men dominated the business side of life. Ladies on the other hand involved themselves in local activities and events, assisted tenants and local communities, as well as running their households. Henrietta McInroy was a lady of this ilk. She did however travel and at one time visited the West Indies; possibly sailing from Liverpool.

After the death of Dr William Stewart Irvine in 1893, Henrietta McInroy had a conversation with the President of the District Nursing Association, Dr Beatty. The conversation greatly interested her, especially the issue of employing a district nurse in the local area, and very soon she started to raise funds with the help of other local ladies. These included:

Mrs Grant Fergusson
Miss Forbes (Honorary Superintendent).
Miss Maxwell
Miss Mitchell
Miss Emma Molyneux (President and Honorary Treasurer).
Miss Renny
Miss Marion Stirling Stuart (Honorary Secretary).

(Census information from that period suggests that Henrietta McInroy and Emma Molyneux would have known each other socially as they moved in similar circles. The former's family were importers, and the latter's father was a stockbroker, both in the Manchester and Liverpool areas. Henrietta McInroy certainly joined in with the local elite who visited Pitlochry and elsewhere in Perthshire. Her travels no doubt resulted in her meeting many different people some of whom would be

Charles McInroy.

eager to call upon her during tours of Scotland and would likely have been taken along to Emma Molyneux's many social gatherings.)

In 1895, the first district nurse (Nurse Anderson) arrived in Pitlochry. She was unfortunately not accepted with enthusiasm – the unknown is always doubted. However, the new medical aid was over time accepted and well appreciated by all, as is evidenced by the subsequent opening of a nursing home.

It is worth including at this point a note of information provided to the author by Charles McInroy (great-nephew of Henrietta McInroy). Charles McInroy was for ten years or so Secretary and Treasurer of the Scottish Branch of the Queen's Nursing Institute, so called because it grew out of a scheme for nursing the sick and poor at home at the bequest of Queen Victoria in her Jubilee Year (1887). The Scottish Branch was established in 1889.

'A Century of Community Caring' Christmas Card, 1989.

The 'Queen's Nurses', the original district nurses, were trained in Castle Terrace, Edinburgh, and it was up to local committees to make arrangements for employing and housing them and providing them with transport. So, in 1895, Pitlochry was among the first districts to take advantage of the scheme. Charles McInroy's late mother, Marjory Walford, was on the Dunkeld committee in the 1920s; it can be said that Henrietta McInroy began what became a family trait. The bookend of this familial trait is that Charles McInroy attended the opening of the new community hospital in Pitlochry with his daughter Alison on 23rd September 2008.

In August 1896, an article was placed in the local press.

The Late Dr W. S. Irvine

The following is the text of the appeal for funds for the purpose of providing a suitable memorial to the late Dr W. S. Irvine of Craigatin:

"All who had the privilege of calling the late Dr Irvine friend and medical adviser, are invited to aid in raising a sum towards a 'useful' and lasting memorial of love and respect for one, who in the wide district of Atholl, for exactly 60 years, lived as a benefactor to all around him. His was a true, an unselfish; a devoted life. He knew his work thoroughly; did it well and with all his might. His power for good was untold, and it seems as if the blank can never be adequately filled. Feeling sure of general approval of this appeal, an opportunity will be given to all who loved and esteemed our 'Dear Old Dr' to contribute. Smallest sums as gratefully received as the larger ones expected."

Contributions will be received by the banks in Pitlochry, Mr Henry Ferguson, East End; Messrs McNaughton, West End; Mr Fisher, Hotel; Miss Molyneux, Tom-na-Monachan; Miss Forbes, Larchwood; and Miss McInroy.

[*Perthshire Advertiser*, 8 August 1896]

In 1897, Henrietta McInroy proposed that a nursing home should be built, and it would prove a suitable memorial to the late Dr Irvine. To this end, Henrietta McInroy and Emma Molyneux set out to raise £500 to provide a home for the district nurse and accommodation for at least two patients. Again, an advert was placed in the *Perthshire Advertiser*.

The Proposed Irvine Home

The movement to perpetuate in some tangible manner the memory of the late Dr W. S. Irvine, which it is suggested might take the form of a sick home, has met with considerable success, and Miss McInroy, the Treasurer of the fund is desirous that any who intend to contribute thereto will intimate their intentions as early as possible in order that the subscription list may be closed.

[*Dundee Advertiser*, 8 January 1897]

Initially Henrietta McInroy had collected money herself throughout the district, but quite soon she was joined by a committee which evolved from the earlier group of ladies. The committee members included:

MRS BARBOUR of Bonskeid
MRS BUTTER of Faskally/Cluniemore
LADY COLQUHOUN of Knockfar
MISS JANE COWAN of Lagreach
MR J. GRANT FERGUSSON of Baledmund
MR JOHN LEONARD, Architect
MISS HENRIETTA MCINROY of Lude
MISS EMMA MOLYNEUX of Tom-na-Monachan
MISS MURRAY of Sonamore
MR AND MRS SANDEMAN of Fonab (Port-na-Craig)
LADY HELEN STEWART MURRAY (Sister of the Duke of Atholl)
There was a gratifying response:
MRS BARBOUR of Bonskeid – £50 Donation.
MISS JANE CAVAN of Lagreach – A bed.
MR J. GRANT FERGUSSON of Baledmund – A site for the nursing home (the location was deemed suitable in every respect).
MR JOHN LEONARD – His services free as architect.
MISS EMMA MOLYNEUX of Tom-na-Monachan – Publication and sale of booklets about Dr Irvine.
MRS MURRAY of Sonamore – £530 Raised.
MR AND MRS SANDEMAN of Fonab (Port-na-Craig) – Organisation of a fete at Fonab House (today Fonab Castle).

Although the site provided for the nursing home was deemed suitable, difficulties were encountered. These and other hinderances which arose meant the building was not completed until 1901, when the nursing home became a fact.

By 1901, £800 had been collected, but £1,400 in total was required, so the committee decided to have a two-day fund-raising event with a bazaar, of which Lady Colquhoun of Knockfarrie was put in 'general charge'. The following poster was displayed:

**TWO DAY BAZAAR
AT PITLOCHRY PUBLIC HALL
IN AID OF
IRVINE MEMORIAL NURSING HOME
STARTING FRIDAY THE 24TH OF AUGUST 1901**

**FRIDAY
OPENING CEREMONY 12 NOON
BAZAAR TO BE OPENED BY
SIR ALEXANDER MUIR MACKENZIE
AFTERNOON CONCERT IN LESSER HALL
WITH FURTHER DRAMATIC ENTERTAINMENT
IN EVENING**

**SATURDAY
OPENING CEREMONY 12 NOON
BAZAAR TO BE OPENED BY
THE VERY REVEREND NORMAN MACLEOD
BAZAAR IN PUBLIC HALL**

**AFTERNOON
A PLAY: *SWEETHEARTS* BY W. S. GILBERT
IN THE LESSER HALL
EVENING
A CONCERT IN LESSER HALL
AUCTION AT 9 P.M. IN PUBLIC HALL**

The two-day event raised £286 14s 5d each day, totalling £573 8s 10d. This amount in addition to the £800 already raised gave a grand total of £1,373 8s 10d which was brought to a final total of £1,436 5s 6d by Mrs Butter of Faskally/Cluniemore with her fund-raising efforts. After the building of the home, furnishing and equipment, £1,376 5s 6d had been spent, leaving a balance of £60 in the capital account.

All who shared in the establishment of the home rejoiced to see how their hopes had been realised, and it continued to grow as an asset to the community under the leadership of the committee and Lady Helen Stewart Murray, who had taken over as president after the death of Henrietta McInroy in 1898. By 1902, ill health was also preventing Emma Molyneux from continuing on the committee.

On 14th July 1902, the nursing home, dedicated to the memory of Dr W. S. Irvine, MD, FRCSE, was opened by the Reverend Duncan Campbell BD of St Matthew's Church, Edinburgh. Although Henrietta McInroy had died four-and-a-half years earlier, her name remained on the list of committee members. (Henrietta McInroy is buried in the family section of Kilmaveonaig Kirkyard, Blair Atholl; her grave lies at the rear of the church by the back wall in the family plots.)

Kilmaveonaig Kirkyard, Blair Atholl.

OPENING OF NURSING HOME AT PITLOCHRY

The public inauguration of the Irvine Memorial Nursing Home, Pitlochry, took place yesterday afternoon. The Home is the outcome of an effort originated by the late Miss H. C. McInroy of Lude. Imbued with a feeling that the name and memory of the late Dr William Stewart Irvine, Craigatin, should in some manner be honourably perpetuated in the district, Miss McInroy before her death had to a large degree, by her personal energies and enthusiasm amongst her friends and the people who knew the late doctor, formed the nucleus of a capital fund, now nearly £1,500. The cost of the buildings amounts to £1,876 5s 6d. Many handsome gifts in the way of furnishings for the Home have been made by the ladies interested. A tablet at the entrance to the Home bears the following inscription:— *"Irvine Memorial Nursing Home. In memory of William Stewart Irvine, M.D., F.R.S.C.E., who was for over 50 years the beloved physician of the Vale of Atholl. Erected by many grateful friends and patients, 1901."*

Henrietta McInroy's gravestone in Kilmaveonaig Kirkyard.

Mr J. Leonard, Pitlochry, was the architect. The Revd Mr Donald introduced the Revd Duncan Campbell, BD, St Matthew's, Edinburgh, who formally opened the new building, and expressed the hope that it would be a centre of healing and Christian influence for generations yet to come. (Applause.)

[*Dundee Courier*, 15 July 1902]

NOTES ON THE McINROY FAMILY TREE

1. **James McInroy:** *b.* 12 August 1759, *d.* 12 July 1825. James McInroy bought Lude in 1821, with the Robertsons in the process of financial collapse due to legal bills. *'James McInroy, one of the nabobs, into the origins of whose fortune it was unwise to look too closely, would buy their (Robertsons') estate which had been in their hands since the 1500s. The estate was bought from under the Duke of Athole's nose.'*

2. **Elizabeth Moore:** *b.* 2 May 1782, *d.* 29 November 1870. Wife of James McInroy (1).

3. **James Patrick McInroy:** *b.* 1799, *d.* 1878. Married Margaret Seton Little (4). James Patrick McInroy inherited Lude in 1825.

4. **Margaret Seton Little:** *b.* 9 November 1799, *d.* 1879.

5. **Elizabeth McInroy:** *b.* 10 January 1801, *d.* 4 January 1808.

6. **William McInroy:** *b.* 1804, *d.* 1896. William McInroy was married but no issue. He bought Shierglass and Arnhall in East Lothian.

7. **Charles Hagart McInroy:** *b.* 21 June 1810, *d.* 13 March 1819.

8. **James McInroy:** *b.* 1823, *d.* 1909. Disinherited, James McInroy had two sons, James William and Harold Percy, and a daughter, Olga Enid, who married Hendrikus Hessling, who had a son Nicolaas (Nick) Hessling.

9. **Henrietta Caroline McInroy:** *b.* 13 June 1828 in Renfrew, *d.* 15 January 1898 in Pitlochry. Henrietta McInroy lived in Kinnaird, Pitlochry, with her niece Debonnaire (1862-1946).

10. **William McInroy:** *b.* 1830, *d.* 1916. William McInroy married Debonnaire Fleetwood from Hesketh They had two sons and five daughters, including Debonnaire (9). He inherited Shierglass and Arnhall from his Uncle William (6).

THE McINROY FAMILY TREE

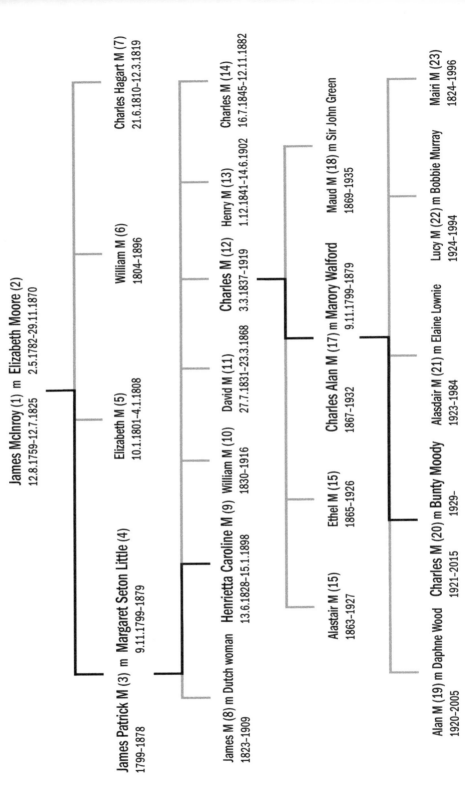

James McInroy (1) m Elizabeth Moore (2)
12.8.1759–12.7.1825   2.5.1782–29.11.1870

Charles Hagart M (7)
21.6.1810–12.3.1819

Charles M (14)
16.7.1845–12.11.1882

William M (6)
1804–1896

Elizabeth M (5)
10.1.1801–4.1.1808

Henry M (13)
1.12.1841–14.6.1902

Charles M (12)
3.3.1837–1919

Maud M (18) m Sir John Green
1869–1935

Mairi M (23)
1824–1996

James Patrick M (3) m Margaret Seton Little (4)
1799–1878   9.11.1799–1879

David M (11)
27.7.1831–23.3.1868

Charles Alan M (17) m Marory Walford
1867–1932   9.11.1799–1879

Lucy M (22) m Bobbie Murray
1924–1994

James M (8) m Dutch woman   Henrietta Caroline M (9)   William M (10)
1823–1909   13.6.1828–15.1.1898   1830–1916

Ethel M (15)
1865–1926

Alasdair M (21) m Elaine Lownie
1923–1984

Alastair M (15)
1863–1927

Charles M (20) m Bunty Moody
1921–2015   1929–

Alan M (19) m Daphne Wood
1920–2005

11. **David McInroy:** *b.* 27 July 1831, *d.* 23 March 1868.
12. **Charles McInroy:** *b.* 3 March 1837, *d.* 1919. Charles McInroy inherited The Burn in 1896.
13. **Henry McInroy:** *b.* 1 December 1841, *d.* 14 June 1902
14. **Patrick McInroy:** *b.* 16 July 1845, *d.* 12 November 1882. Patrick McInroy married and had a son and a daughter
15. **Alastair McInroy:** *b.* 1863, *d.* 1927. Disinherited.
16. **Ethel McInroy:** *b.* 1865, *d.* 1926.
17. **Charles Alan McInroy:** *b.* 1867, *d.* 1932. Charles Alan McInroy married Marjory Walford. He inherited The Burn in 1919 and sold the property in 1921.
18. **Maud McInroy:** *b.* 1869, *d.* 1935. Maud McInroy married Admiral Sir John Green.
19. **Alan McInroy:** *b.* 1921, *d.* 2005. Alan McInroy married Daphne Wood (*née* Weston).
20. **Charles McInroy:** *b.* 1921, *d.* 2015. Charles McInroy married 'Bunty' Moody. Together they had two sons and two daughters. He was the great-nephew of Henrietta McInroy (9). Charles McInroy attended the opening of the new community hospital at Bobbin Mill in 2008.
21. **Alasdair McInroy:** *b.* 1923, *d.* 1984. Alasdair McInroy married Elaine Lowie.
22. **Lucy McInroy:** *b.* 1924, *d.* 1994. Lucy McInroy married Bobbie Murray.
23. **Mairi McInroy:** *b.* 1924, *d.* 1996.

CHAPTER FOUR

Miss Emma Molyneux
(Molyneux, meaning 'Little Mills')

E
MMA MOLYNEUX was born on 4th December 1849 in Cavendish Terrace, Princes Park, Toxteth Park, in the County of Lancaster. She was baptised on 12th January 1850 in St Paul's, Princes Park, Liverpool. Her birth was registered on 9th January 1850 in West Derby (then Lancashire) by her father John Blayds Molyneux, just seven months after the death of her older sister Fanny. Emma's mother, Emma Susan Molyneux, NÉE Potts, died shortly after Emma's birth; her father was a noted 'general broker'. In 1851, he became a 'cotton broker' for Molyneux, Taylor & Company of 7 Upper Canning Street, Liverpool.

Census information reveals that during her life Emma moved around different family members.

1851: Aged 2 – Living with her father and her grandmother, Ann Potts, at 32 Watergate Street, Toxteth.

1861: Aged 12 – Living in her uncle Thomas Lancaster's house in Stroud.

1871: Aged 21 – Still living with her uncle in Stroud.

1881: Aged 31 – Lodging at 31 Cambridge Street, Paddington, Marylebone.

1891: Aged 41 – Once again staying with her Uncle Thomas Lancaster at Bownham House in Rodborough, both living on their own means.

1901: Aged 51 – No census information available.

1911: Aged 61 – Living at Manor Court, Harefield, Middlesex.

Sometime in 1890, Emma came to Pitlochry and on this initial visit she must have decided to move to the area, for in 1897 she bought fourteen acres of ground to the west of Pitlochry and north of the railway line.

This ground was almost opposite Craigatin (Dr Irvine's house). On this ground, Emma built a large house, Tom-na-Monachan (Irish for Molyneux), with the help of building firm Jamieson, Stewart & Forbes. Emma wrote:

> I saw no reason to forgo the finer side of life and put in an elegant white marble staircase which could be viewed from the gallery as well as the Hall below. I also added the luxury of a white marble bath.

Tom-na-Monachan.

Emma seemed to live a busy life and continued to move around the British Isles. Having built Tom-na-Monachan, she stayed on fourteen years, but in that time, in collaboration with Henrietta McInroy, helped bring about a nursing association, district nurse, cottage hospital and, according to the records of the local Episcopalian church magazine (from 1903), made a number of contributions:

JANUARY 1903: Miss Molyneux gave £50 and the promise of a further £20 for a new organ.

DECEMBER 1903: Miss Molyneux gave £5 donation towards an organists' stipend.

SEPTEMBER 1905: By kind invitation of Miss Molyneux a most successful drawing-room meeting was held at Tom-na-Monachan.

APRIL 1908: Miss Molyneux sent flowers to decorate for Easter at Holy Trinity Church, Pitlochry, and Kilmaveonaig Church, Blair Atholl.

APRIL 1908: By kind permission Miss Molyneux held a Sunday School treat at Tom-na-Monachan.

Emma also commissioned and gifted a smaller copy of the font in St Nicholas Collegiate Church (now the Church of Ireland) in Galway to

Portrait of Emma Molyneux (signature inset).

Kilmaveonaig Church in Blair Atholl. (This suggests that Emma Molyneux's family might have had a connection with the Irish Molyneux families, although the records in this regard are patchy.) A description of the font in St Nicholas is found in James Hardiman's *The History of the Town and County of the Town of Galway. From the Earliest Period to the Present Time (1820)*.

> A very ancient circular baptismal font of black marble is still preserved in the church. It rests on an antique sculptured base, and is ornamented with Gothic work, trefoils, amongst which the figure of an Irish wolf-dog appears engraved.
>
> The baptismal font is late 16th/early 17th century, although the Church dates from 1320 and was possibly built on an earlier site.

There is little doubt that Emma was heavily involved in the social life of the local community. One possibility for her being what appears to be an active 'social hostess' is that many summer visitors to the Pitlochry area were people already known to her through having lived in many areas of the UK. Her many guests included:

PROFESSOR J. STUART BLACKIE: A scholar of languages who also holidayed in Kinnaird Cottage, as well as latterly leasing the gate cottage at Tom-na-Monachan when his health was failing. In July 1894, Emma presented Professor Blackie with 85 roses for his 85th birthday, but sadly in 1895 he died.

MARIE CORELLI: A popular writer of books of romance in this era, who often stayed at Coille Brochan Cottage. Among her books are included: *A Romance of Two Worlds* (1886), *The Sorrows of Satan* (1895), *The Mighty Atom* (1896) and *The Master-Christian* (1900).

BEATRIX POTTER: Who although holidayed in Birnam, was friendly with Professor Blackie and Dr William Irvine.

ROBERT LOUIS STEVENSON: Who lived for a while in Kinnaird Cottage, where it is thought he wrote *Thrawn Janet* (1881) and *The Merry Men* (1882).

Emma Molyneux's headstone: 'In memory of Emma Molyneux, Daughter of the Late John Blayds Molyneux, Lady of Grace of the Order of St John of Jerusalem in England. Died 11th August 1936. By the Faith of Jesus Christ – Blessed Hope'.

An issue which has proved impossible to resolve is the title on Emma's gravestone: 'Lady of Grace of the Order of St John of Jerusalem in England'. Emma was admitted to the Order as a Lady of Grace (equivalent to a Knight of Grace) on 16th March 1917. According to the Chapter General Minutes in the Museum and Library of the Order of St John in London, Emma was proposed for admission by The Hon. Sir Arthur Stanley (head of the British Red Cross Society and Chairman of the Joint War Committee of the BRCS and the Order of St John) and Sir John Furley (Deputy Chairman of the St John Ambulance Association). Her lady sponsors were Lady Furley (a keen worker for the Red Cross and Order of St John) and Lady Perrot (the Lady Superintendent-in-Chief nursing divisions, St John

Ambulance Brigade). But no reason is given for Emma Molyneux's admission!

Emma's only other connection with the Order of St John was a contribution of £5 to the St John Ambulance Association in 1902, which made her a life member. There is no mention of her work in any of the reports of the association's Scottish centres (St Andrew's Ambulance Association took over from St John north of the Scottish border in 1903).

At the time Emma was admitted to the Order of St John, there were several grades of membership. According to the *Bye Laws and Regulations of the Order* published in 1916, a Lady of Grace differed from a Lady of Justice in that the latter had produced proof of coats of arms won by her parents and grandparents. Ladies of Grace did not do this because they were either unable to or did not feel it was necessary to do so. The whole system was overhauled in 1926 when a Royal Charter superseded those of 1888 and 1907 and, among others, the title of Dame of Grace replaced Lady of Grace. In 1999, there were five grades of membership:

Bailiff /Dame Grand Cross
Knight/Dame of Justice/Grace
Commander Brother/Sister
Officer Brother/Sister
Serving Brother/Sister.

Emma may well have been engaged during the First World War in voluntary aid to the sick and wounded at home as well as abroad. Unfortunately, there is no evidence to this end within the records and archives of the Wellcome Trust, British Red Cross, Florence Nightingale Museum Trust nor the London Metropolitan Archives.

Even though Emma appears to have left Pitlochry around 1908/9, Tom-na-Monachan seems to have been owned by her until 1916, when it was bought by a Turkish national, Yervent Hagot Iskender, to be used as a Turkish consulate. Iskender, a mine broker, who resided at that time in Paris, subsequently sold the property – in 1923 – to Commander Henry Dewhurst, a cotton manufacturer. In 1935, the property was bought by Diana Adams who sold it after only six months to Pine Trees Pitlochry Ltd.

The 1901 Census details the house staff at Tom-na-Monachan:

TOM-NA-MONACHAN:
JAMES JOHNSTONE: Gardener, aged 47.
MARGARET JOHNSTONE: Gardener's wife, aged 47
JESSIE JOHNSTONE: Daughter of James and Margaret, aged 20.
MARJORY McLAUCHLAN: Housemaid, aged 27.
TOM-NA-MONACHAN LODGE: Unoccupied.

TOM-NA-MONACHAN STABLES:
WILLIAM MACDONALD: Coachman, aged 49.
BETSY MACDONALD: Coachman's wife, aged 50.

A brief history of Manor Court along with a description of the property during Emma's residence is provided next.

1664: Built in 1664 as a farm house named Marlowes. John Sly paid rent to the Lord of the Manor. He compiled a tax list of hearths and chimneys; Manor Court had six hearths.
1681: Rented by Robert Mossendew.
1699: Farmed by his widow Francis Mossendew. A hundred years later, the house was renamed Conduit Farm and farmed by William Trowper.
1861: Held by James Martin, who died in 1879.
1889: Owned by Charles Brown, a builder and decorator. The house was renamed Manor House.
1911: Emma Molyneux living at Manor Court as owner.
1913: Still occupied by Emma.

Mrs Jane P. Mennell along with Mr D. H. Mitchell (both of Harefield) provided information about Manor Court. Mrs Mennell has lived in Harefield most of her life, and as a young child was taken to Manor Court to visit for tea. She described the house as very comfortable; and having a dining room near the domestic quarters which was not large. There was another room, also not very large. The drawing room was reached by stairs going down. This was a lovely room and Mrs Mennell recalled her mother being told by Emma that the drawing room had once been a barn. She also recalled being entertained by playing 'Blow Football', and at other times by a delightful musical box decorated with small animals playing musical instruments. In addition, the grounds were lovely with a little stream (the conduit) and a bridge and nearby were located a garage and outbuildings, with a cupola above. Emma lived with a companion, Miss Tweedie; the chauffeur lived in a cottage across the road from Manor Court. Manor Court was a much smaller house than Tom-na-Monachan.

Emma remained on the Harefield Parish Church Council and attended meetings regularly until 1933. Latterly, she also arranged a Molyneux Trust Fund (of value around £250) for the church, assumedly for the churchyard upkeep.

Eventually, Manor Court was taken over by Hillingdon Borough Council and (sadly) altered by extensions to provide 40 flats for the borough's homeless. A number of years later, it housed nursing Sisters from Harefield Hospital.

The Pine Trees Hotel, Pitlochry, formerly Tom-na-Monachan.

From time to time, Emma returned to Pitlochry to visit Mrs Jamieson of Craighulan and Mrs Jessie Gordon of Glenrinnes, Atholl Road, whose grandfather had built Tom-na-Monachan with the firm of Jamieson, Stewart & Forbes. On 11th August 1936, Emma died at Manor Court of cerebral thrombosis and arterio-sclerosis. Emma's death was reported in the *Perthshire Advertiser* of 19th August 1936:

Death of Former Pitlochry Resident
A Good Friend to the Community

The death of Miss Molyneux, formerly of Tomnamonachan, Pitlochry, took place, after an illness of four months, at Manor Court, Harefield, Middlesex, on Tuesday.

The interment took place in the village churchyard there.

Miss Molyneux built the fine mansion house of Tomnamonachan – now the Pine Trees Hotel – and resided there for many years.

She was a good friend to Holy Trinity Episcopal Church, Pitlochry, and maintained her interest in its welfare up to the end. Miss Molyneux also took an active part in promoting the Nursing Home at Pitlochry – opened in 1902 as a memorial to the late Dr W. S. Irvine, with whom she was on terms of personal friendship.

She also took part in the formation of Pitlochry District Nursing Association, of which she was first president and hon. Treasurer.

THE MOLYNEUX FAMILY TREE

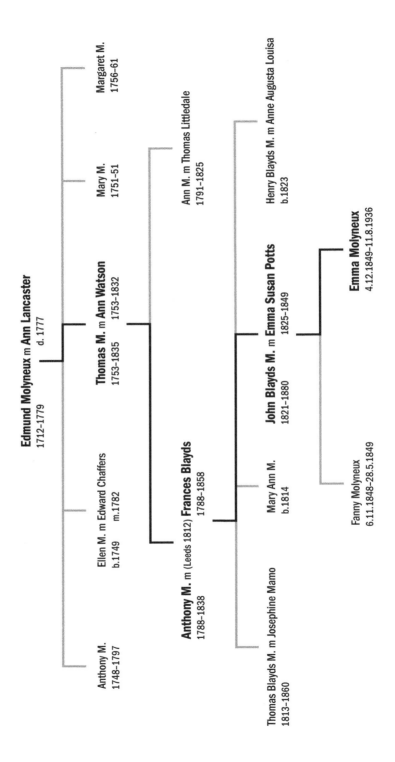

Edmund Molyneux m **Ann Lancaster**
1712–1779   d. 1777

Anthony M.
1748–1797

Ellen M. m Edward Chaffers
b.1749   m.1782

Mary M.
1751–51

Margaret M.
1756–61

Thomas M. m **Ann Watson**
1753–1835   1753–1832

Ann M. m Thomas Littledale
1791–1825

Anthony M. m (Leeds 1812) **Frances Blayds**
1788–1838   1788–1858

Henry Blayds M. m Anne Augusta Louisa
b.1823

Mary Ann M.
b.1814

John Blayds M. m **Emma Susan Potts**
1821–1880   1825–1849

Thomas Blayds M. m Josephine Mamo
1813–1860

Fanny Molyneux
6.11.1848–28.5.1849

Emma Molyneux
4.12.1849–11.8.1936

SELECTED TIMELINE FOR
THE PARISH OF MOULIN, 1832-92

1832: A road bridge was built over the River Tummel.

1834: Clunie Bridge was built for road traffic.

1836: The River Garry Bridge was built. (The ferry at Portnacraig still ran until 1913, when on Empire Day it made its final journey before the suspension bridge was opened. The bridge was paid for by public subscription and a grant from Highland District Council.)

1836: Both the Commercial Bank of Scotland and the Central Bank of Scotland (later to become the Bank of Scotland in 1868) opened branches, the latter on Mid Moulin Road or Bonnethill Road, which is today a branch of the Trustee Savings Bank. In addition, the business of the National Security Savings Bank of Edinburgh was conducted by the Manager of the Commercial Bank.

1839: Fisher's Hotel was established.

1839: A brewery was erected, which operated until about 1870. Its name survives in the Brewery Cottages (Cloichard), to which the brewery was converted.

1844: Pitlochry and the surrounding area grew in prosperity due to the visit by Queen Victoria to Blair Castle. In the company with Queen Victoria was her Royal Physician who held the air and climate of the area with such a high opinion he recommended people to holiday in the area. Sir James Simpson, a famous Edinburgh doctor, also praised the climate as did J. D. McCulloch author of *The Scenery of Dunkeld and Blair Atholl* (1823). This meant Pitlochry started to become a tourist area.

1846: Carr's of Carlisle sent specially-made ships biscuits (a better quality and packed more carefully than the original ships biscuits) to help alleviate the poverty and starvation in the Highlands and Islands.

1858: The Perth Banking Company began in business in 'Old Bank Business' at the West End (Atholl Road). It was later taken over by the Union Bank of Scotland. In 1890, it was transferred to buildings in the centre of Pitlochry, and then in 1955 was absorbed by the Bank of Scotland. All these bank openings were mainly caused by the influx of visitors to the area. This time also saw the building of some of the now present Victorian villas.

1863: The first Ordnance Survey map was compiled. It was 6" to 25" to the mile scale, surveyed in 1863 and published in 1867. It showed Pitlochry still a village of limited extent. The Central Bank of Scotland was the last house on Mid Moulin Road and the Dye Works, later to be MacNaughton's Tweed Mill and today the Co-operative supermarket, was the last in West Moulin Road until Croft Machaig. A smithy was at its present position at the West End.

The road from Perth, until the building of the railway, proceeded by what is now the drive to Dundarroch and a milestone (Perth 27 miles, Blair Atholl 7½ miles) is situated on what is now Bruach Lane. There were no houses east of the Union Bank of Scotland. Toberargan existed east of the Star Inn (now Scotland's Hotel). There were only four houses on Lower Oakfield beyond the Free Church (now flats opposite Jubilee Place). Well Brae and Knockard Road did not exist and there were no buildings between Rose Cottage and Tomnamoan, which was then a small farm, near which was a well. What were paths are now roads.

At Auchnahyle, there was a malt house and a kiln. Auchnahyle was the birthplace and home of Alexander Duff. A mill dam and sluice controlled water, supplied to a distillery at 'Mains of Pitlochrie', no longer there but the site of the present Blair Athol Distillery. Farina Mill was on the Black Spout burn just east of the railway. At Milton of Edradour (lay as it does today) Edradour Distillery and also a lint mill.

A 'Caisteal Dubh' is shown north-west of Tomnamoan. This was a small circular enclosure of dry stones about ten feet high – it is thought to be on the site of the house called Am Laimhrig. This was occupied by Dr Anderson whose family transferred the name to their present house at the corner of Broom Place and East Moulin Road. Caisteal Dubh should not be confused with Caisteal Dubh Mhaothlinne (the Black Castle of Moulin).

Cnoc Fairidh is a small hill near Trinity Episcopal Church. Knock-farrie was built on this site. Cnoc an Ro-aire was beside the Union Bank and Cnoc Dubh was beside West Moulin Road where Knockard Road now meets it.

On West Moulin Road, there were no houses between Croftmechaig and Tychlodich. There was an old lime kiln beside the sluice where Craigmore now stands. The post office was on the site of what is now Davidson's Chemist at the corner of West Moulin Road.

A saw mill sat beside the gas works; amongst other items, the saw mill provided the wood for the mill which made bobbins for the spinning of cotton and wool. When Dr Irvine came to Pitlochry, before the railway was built, the area south of the main road as far as the gas works was a market garden and orchard. After the railway was built, the ground between the railway and the main road became a Memorial Garden.

At Moulin, there was a school (there was no Moulin Hall). There were buildings to the south-east and east of the churchyard. In Moulin Square, there was a pump (there should now be a flagstone in the grass marking the spot). A smithy was at the east side of the square. Ballinlochan and Balnadrum Farms both had circular horse mills on their northern sides.

In the summer of 1863, the various railway lines joined up, making it possible to travel from Perth to Inverness. This enabled Dr Irvine to visit his patients north and south by train, but east and west still required horseback. In 1863, four trains a day left Perth: 6.45 am, 9.30 am, 1.00 pm, and 4.10 pm; arriving at Inverness at 1.45 pm, 3.45 pm, 7.00 pm, and 10.40 pm. There was an additional train from Perth at 7.30pm for Blair Athole, due at 9.05 pm.

1865: Killiecrankie Station opened on 3rd July.

1867: Dr Robert Irvine, William Irvine's nephew, joined him in the practice. Robert was the son of William's older brother Alexander, the minister of Blair Atholl.

1875: Athole Palace was built as a hydro; and opened in 1878.

1889: A Celtic cross was erected in memory of Alexander Duff, born, and brought up in Moulin, who became a missionary in India. The cross stands on the east side of the Church of Scotland building.

1892: Fonab House was built by the Sandeman family (of Sandeman Port fame). Later this building became known as Port-na-Craig House and was the Control Centre for the North of Scotland Hydro Electric Board (later Scottish Hydro-Electric) until 2001. It is now Fonab Castle Hotel.

CHAPTER FIVE

The Story of the
Irvine Memorial Hospital – 1901-2018

I N 1901, the Irvine Memorial Hospital was well on the way to being completed. Unfortunately, Henrietta McInroy had died, and Emma Molyneux had handed over to Lady Helen Stewart Murray. The two ladies were nonetheless still listed on the committee, which continued to encourage gifts and donations. This chapter offers a history of the Irvine Memorial Hospital from 1901 until 2018 through a series of excerpts from newspaper reports, publications, and minutes.

1901
Donations in Preparation for the opening of the Hospital

MRS BARBOUR of Bonskeid – £10 donation and six pillowcases.

MISS JANE COWAN of Lagreach – Breakfast and tea services.

MRS FERGUSSON of Baledmund – Six sheets.

MRS GWYER – A bed, bedding, and an invalid couch.

MISS HUMPHREY – One-and-a-half dozen towels.

MRS MACLEAN – A bolster and four pillows.

MRS MAXWELL – A dinner service.

MRS K. I. MAXWELL – An adjustable bed table.

MISS MITCHELL – One dozen small and a half-dozen large tray cloths.

MISS EMMA MOLYNEUX of Tom-na-Monachan – The defrayment of the cost of the memorial tablet to be affixed to the hospital.

MISS MOREHEAD – Two large tables.

THE PITLOCHRY WOMEN'S GUILD OF THE CHURCH OF SCOTLAND (Dorcas Branch) – Three pairs of sheets, one large rubber sheet, three bolster-C, three pillow cases, three bandages, and two flannelette nightdresses.

The Irvine Memorial Nursing Home, 1902.

1902

The Opening Ceremony

The opening ceremony was on Monday, 14th July 1902 and commenced with the hymn 'O God, Our Help', and the Home was formally inaugurated by the Reverend Duncan Campbell B.D., St Matthew's Church, Edinburgh. The building is in the domestic style of architecture, the walls being harled and tinted in a light cream colour. The accommodation consists of male and female wards with separate bathrooms and other conveniences, nurses' rooms, kitchen, and offices. The ceilings are lofty and the whole of the Nursing Home is airy from plans prepared by Mr John Leonard, architect, Pitlochry. The amount expended on the Home, including furnishings to date is £1,376 5s 6d, there being a balance at the credit of capital account of £60. There was a large attendance.

The hymn 'O God, Our Help' having been sung and prayer offered, the Rev D. M. Donald B.D. read a letter of apology for absence from Miss Molyneux, Tom-na-monachan, who said it was a grievous disappointment that, in obedience to doctor's orders, she was unable to be present at the inauguration of the Home, which she trusted would keep Dr Irvine's memory green for generations. Apologies for absence were also read from Sir Alexander Muir Mackenzie, Bart, of Delvine, Mr James Ramsay, Balhousie Castle (who enclosed a subscription) and Mrs Butter (late of Faskally). Introducing Mr Campbell (who is a son of the late minister of Moulin), Mr Donald expressed regret at the absence of Miss Molyneux who had had the scheme so much at heart.

In declaring the building open, Mr Campbell said he appreciated the privilege of inaugurating that memorial because of his sincere respect and esteem for the distinguished physician whose valuable services it commemorated, and because of his deep interest in all that concerned the parish of Moulin. The whole countryside was proud of Dr Irvine, and had absolute faith in his skill, and what a countryside he represented from Rannoch and Dalnacardoch on the west to Strathardle and Glenshee on the east, with a score of interesting glens to right and left. It was, he proceeded, a happy thought to link his memory with that nursing home, the inauguration of which he understood was due to one who was herself an indefatigable philanthropist in her day – the late Miss McInroy, Sonamore. He congratulated Miss Molyneux, the committee, and the many generous donors on being able to open the home free of debt, and he had no doubt in the future it would be supported so that it would realise the noble and holy mission for which it was designed (applause).

The Revd Canon Bowstead thereafter brought the proceedings to a close with the benediction.

Presentation to a Nurse

An interesting private function took place thereafter, when Nurse Anderson was made the recipient of a handsome writing bureau bearing the inscription: *"Presented to Nurse Anderson at the opening of the Irvine Memorial Nursing Home by the Committee of the Pitlochry Nursing Association in grateful appreciation of her valued services in the district during the past 6 years – 1902."* Mrs Barbour of Bonskeid conveyed the gift to Nurse Anderson who expressed appreciation of the kindness shown her.

1903

Rules for Nursing in Home

1. The Irvine Memorial Nursing Home is for cases of non-infectious disease or accident and patients will be received on the recommendation of any of the Medical Men in Pitlochry provided there are vacant beds at the time.

2. A weekly payment from 5/– upwards shall be required from each patient towards the cost of maintenance, exclusive of medicines and medical attention and the Secretary; but one bed being endowed to a patient shall be free on recommendation of any of the resident Medical Men.

3. Patients must at all times comply with the orders of the Medical Attendant and Nurses under penalty of removal.

4. No article of food or drink shall be brought into the Home without the permission of the Nurses.

5. One Lady Member of the Committee shall undertake in rotation, or as may be arranged, to visit the Home once a week when she shall thoroughly inspect the Home and shall see the patients without the presence of the Nurses.

6. Visitors will be admitted on Tuesdays, Thursdays and Sundays from Two to Four p.m. and from Seven to Eight p.m. Visitors from a distance will be admitted on written permission from the Medical Men in attendance, or at the discretion of the Nurses. Patients may be visited at any time by a Clergyman.

Pitlochry Nursing Association

The first annual general meeting of the subscribers to the Irvine Memorial Home and Pitlochry District Nursing Association was held yesterday in the Public Hall – Mr Hugh Mitchell, solicitor, presiding. The financial support for the past year, showing an income of £188 3s 1d and expenditure of £132 16s 2d, was read and approved. Mr Mitchell pointed out that in future the expenditure would be rather more, as two nurses are now employed instead of one as formerly. Miss Douglas, Rosemount; Mrs Colquhoun, Old Faskally; and Mrs Cooke, The Rectory, were selected members of committee three of whom retire annually.

25th January 1903 – Christmas Gifts

The Secretary of the Irvine Memorial Nursing Home, Pitlochry, was in attendance yesterday for the purpose of receiving Christmas gifts of greetings and other goods. A considerable number manifested their interest in the Home by contributing useful parcels.

The Committee of the Irvine Memorial Nursing Home, Pitlochry, having solicited gifts to that institution as Christmas tokens of goodwill, the appeal was met with a most hearty response, and welcome parcels of all sorts and sizes flowed into the Home. The appropriate gift of a large larder was also made by a lady on the same occasion. The committee expresses their gratitude to all who have shown their practical interest by these generous gifts.

1906

Blair Atholl – Pitlochry Nursing Home

In aid of this excellent institution a football match, which created considerable interest, took place on Saturday evening in the Tullibardine Park. The teams were specially selected, and the sum collected amounted to over £3.

Ballinluig Concert

A highly successful concert and dramatic entertainment was given in the Logierait Schoolroom on Friday evening in aid of the Irvine Memorial Nursing Home, Pitlochry. There was a large attendance, and Mr Hugh Mitchell, JP, Pitlochry, presided. The concert opened with a Gaelic song (in three parts) by the Logierait Junior Gaelic Choir, conducted by Mr James Kennedy. The soloists were Miss Beattie, Pitlochry; Miss Grace Menzies; Miss Dawson, Logierait; and Mr P. Gibb, Aberfeldy. Mr Hugh Macdonald, Pitlochry, danced the Highland Fling and Sword Dance. Mr Duff's string band gave Highland selections at intervals, while Mrs Meldrum, Rosehill, Pitlochry, promoter of the concert, played the accompaniments. The second part was taken up with a comedy in two acts entitled 'All's Fair in Love'. The characters were sustained by Mr A. Clow, solicitor, Aberfeldy; Mr A. R. Macgregor, Aberfeldy; Mr J. Mann, Aberfeldy; Miss Margaret Haggart, Aberfeldy; and Miss Mary Yool, Aberfeldy. The drawings amounted to £14 10s 6d.

1908

Christmas Service and Collection
The work of the Post Office was unusually heavy, and one almost felt sorry for the heavily-laden postmen. The usual Christmas service, conducted by the Revd Donald Lamont, MA, parish minister, took place in the Parish Church. The service was appropriate, and the praise consisted entirely of Christmas carols. There was a good attendance. A collection was taken on behalf of the poor of the parish and the Irvine Memorial Home, Pitlochry.

1909

Rules for Nursing Staff and Employees
Rule Number 20: The Nurse Matron shall be off duty from 2 until 10pm once a week, or in lieu thereof be at liberty to take a weekend (Friday-Monday) once every three months, with the approval of the Medical Men. She shall have one month's holiday yearly, the month to be fixed by the Committee.

1911

11th February 1911 – Matron Wanted
Probationer assistant Matron wanted for Irvine Memorial Home. Apply stating age, experience, to Hon Secretary, Ivybank, Pitlochry.

3rd August 1911 – Annual Meeting
The annual meeting of Subscribers to the Irvine Memorial Nursing Home for Atholl & Pitlochry Nursing Association was held at Pitlochry yesterday afternoon, Mr D. Stewart Fergusson of Dunfallandy presiding.

The report of the president Lady Helen Stewart Murray stated that the work of the Association was progressing most favourably in the district. Sixty patients were treated in the home and 2,776 visits were paid by the district nurse. Moving the adoption of reports, the chairman urged the institution of an Endowment Fund on behalf of the home and said their position might be adversely affected under the insurance Bill. Mr Hugh Mitchell, solicitor, seconding said while such institutions might possibly come under Government supervision under the Bill, this would not be in the best interest of the Home as it usually led to red tape and increased expenditure. He hoped they would be able to continue on a voluntary basis.

1913

8th August 1913 – Pitlochry Nursing Association

The annual meeting of Irvine Memorial Nursing Home for Atholl & Pitlochry Nursing Association was held yesterday, Canon Cook presiding. The Annual Report by the president, Lady Helen Stewart Murray, Blair Castle, bore that the work of the Nursing Home continued to increase. 1,120 visits were paid by the district nurse during the year.

The finances showed the following balances:

Nursing Home	£36 12s 7d against £100 2s 5d in 1912
Endowment Fund	£531 4s 9d
District Nurse balance	£116 19s 7d against £122 19s 9d in 1912
Endowment	£118 13s 6d.

On the motion of Mr Charles Butter of Cluniemore, the reports were approved. Discussion took place as to what sum should be charged to patients of the Home who are receiving sick benefit under the Insurance Act. Mr H. Mitchell, F.S.A, said the effects of the Act, as regards the Home, had not been altogether good. The amount of subscriptions received was less and expenses had increased. He suggested the committee have power to fix charges to be made, taking into consideration the circumstances of each patient. This was agreed to.

1916

7th July 1916 – Free Gift Sales

At the Annual Meeting at Pitlochry of Moulin Agricultural Association – Mr R. Inglis, JP, Old Blair, presiding – it was agreed to hold a free gift sale on Saturday 17th August in aid of patriotic objects. The proceeds of the former sale, amounting to £489 7s 3d were donated as follows: Fonab Auxiliary Hospital, £156 11s 7d; Perthshire War Workers' Association, £100; Perthshire Prisoners of War Fund, £100; Perth Royal Infirmary, £60; Perth Station Barrow, £50; Irvine Memorial Nursing Home, Pitlochry, £25; Perthshire Red Cross £10. In view of the continuance of the war, and the difficulties of transport, it was agreed that no show be held this year. The ordinary accounts showed a credit balance of £109 7s 1d.

Office-bearers were re-elected, with the Duke of Atholl, KT, as patron, and Mr R. Inglis, JP, as president. The following conveners were appointed in connection with the free gift sale: Mr R. Inglis, Mr A. M'Diarmid, Rotmell; Mir John Cameron, Middleton; and Mr Donald Robertson, Strathtummel.

Gifts to Atholl Home
Lady Helen Stewart Murray, Blair Castle, has intimated a donation of £10 towards the Irvine Memorial Nursing Home for Atholl, at Pitlochry, to which Miss Molyneux has already gifted £500. Mrs Robertson, sen., of Auchleeks, has also given a further donation of £10 towards Pitlochry District Nurse Endowment Fund and Miss Robertson, Donnachaidh, £5 to the same fund.

30th August 1916 – Matron Wanted
Matron wanted for Irvine Memorial Nursing Home, Pitlochry, fully certified nurse. Apply, stating age, experience, references to Secretary, Ivybank, Pitlochry.

29th December 1916 – Lady Helen Stewart Murray Weds – Quiet Ceremony in Blair Atholl Parish Church
Owing to the war and the indisposition of the Duke of Atholl, the wedding of Lady Helen Stewart Murray and Mr David Alexander Tod of Braehead, Dunkeld, took place quietly yesterday afternoon in the Parish Church, Blair Atholl, the officiating clergymen being the Rev. Donald Lamont, Blair Atholl, and the Rev. Dr Fleming, Pont Street Church, London. Miss Campbell presided at the organ, while the musical service was led by a choir of children from Blair Atholl and Struan, under the conductorship of Mr Kellock.

Lady Helen, who is the Duke of Atholl's second daughter, is held in high esteem wherever she is known, both on account of the standing of the Atholl family and her own kindly and gracious personality. There was little wonder, therefore, that the deepest interest was manifested in the wedding.

The church was beautifully decorated with flowers and evergreens, and the congregation consisted mainly of deputations from various parts of the Atholl districts and estates representative of the donors of the presentations.

In the absence of the Duke, the Marquis of Tullibardine gave his sister, Lady Helen, away. Instead of the usual processional music, beautiful Highland airs heralded the approach of the bride. She was wearing a lovely gown of white satin, trimmed with Brussels lace, and a Brussels lace veil. There were no bridesmaids. Sheriff J. Dean Leslie acted as best man.

Lady Helen Stewart Murray, 1916.

David Alexander Tod, 1916.

After the service, wedding favours of tartan and juniper (the Murray badge) were distributed by a number of school children, and to the strains of Highland music the bride and bridegroom left the church and motored to Blair Castle, where a few relatives assembled to wish them good luck. Later in the afternoon, Mr Tod and his bride departed by motor to their honeymoon, her Ladyship travelling in a purple cloth dress, with velvet coat to match trimmed with black fur.

Some of the Presents

The presents to the bride included: From the bridegroom – A sapphire and diamond ring, amethyst and diamond pendant, and a sealskin coat with sable collar and muff, From the tenants on the Atholl estates, the Atholl Divisional Council of the Primrose League, and the Atholl Branch of An Comunn Gaidhealach – a portrait in oils of the bride by Mr John Lavery, ARA, RSA.

The estate and household employees on the Atholl estates gave silver entree dishes and a pair of silver sauce boats; the school children on the Atholl estates, including Killiecrankie School, gave a tortoiseshell and silver clock, while the committee and staff of Irvine Memorial Nursing Home, Pitlochry, presented her Ladyship with a silver tankard. Among the presents to the bridegroom was a silver salver and a silver cake basket from the householders of Elm Park and Braehead, and a silver cake basket by the employees at Braehead.

1916–17

Twenty-First Annual Report

The Annual General Meeting of the above Association was held in the Institute Hall, Pitlochry, on Saturday 5th August 1916, at 3 p.m. Captain Graham Dixon, Scottish Horse, presided. There were 23 present. The Chairman said he had been asked by the Officer Commanding at Dunkeld to communicate his thanks for the benefit derived by the men of the Scottish Horse from the Nursing Home when they required treatment, and for the care and attention which the Nurses had given them while there. He was glad to report that £33 had been obtained from the Scottish Horse Sports, which would be available for the Home, and also the sum of £15 from the concert which had been organised by the Canteen Committee with the assistance of the Scottish Horse.

Captain Dixon said that on the whole he thought the report of accounts good, as only one account showed a loss on the year's working, that of the Nursing Home itself. Owing to the war, it was not surprising that the subscriptions of the Nursing Home had fallen, but he hoped that this was only temporary.

Mrs Courtier Dutton, the Matron, has given every satisfaction and her work has been much appreciated at the Nursing Home. She has also supervised the work of the District Nurses.

Mrs Willison, VAD, earned our thanks for her voluntary services; since removal of the soldiers she has left, and the Committee presented her with a carriage clock in recognition of her excellent work.

The Probationer, Nurse McEachnie, has given every satisfaction having done her work well, and we are glad to have found one so willing.

It is gratifying to note that 67 men of the Scottish Horse have been treated in the Nursing Home during the past year, and 38 civilian patients. The District Nurses have attended 77 cases and paid 1,280 visits.

Lady Helen Tod, President.

1918

Gift from Fonab

The Committee's grateful thanks are due to the Commandant and Committee of Fonab Auxiliary Hospital for their most generous gifts including a hut with beds complete from Mr Sandeman, linen stores from Mrs Sandeman and Mrs Butter, sterilizer from Lieut. And Mrs Fergusson of Baledmund, a Glass Dressing Table from the Misses Laughland.

The Committee are also indebted to Mrs Stewart Fergusson, Dunfallandy, for so generously paying the cost of shelving and enclosing the recess in the sitting room at the Home providing a much-needed store cupboard. Mr Tod and I were glad to give a kitchen dresser. Other gifts include:

Load of Manure – Mr G. Brodie
Load of Wood – Mr Taylor
Load of Coal – Mr Stewart-Fergusson
Bag of Potatoes – Mr Scott of Logierait Mill
Screen – Miss J. E. Cowan
Bed Couch – Perth Red Cross Society
Wheelchair – Miss Mathie
Box of Provisions per Pound Day – Logierait Women's Guild
Vegetables and Fruit – Holy Trinity Church Harvest Festival
A Hot Air Cabinet and Several Useful Appliances – Mrs Mackenzie of Torrdarach
Rent of Field Paid Annually – Mr and Mrs Macdonald of Blair Atholl
all of which are gratefully acknowledged.

For the first time in the History of the Nursing Home, the accounts close with a debit balance. It is a matter of regret to the Committee that even with careful management they have been unable to make the income cover the expenditure owing to the increased cost in the price of all Household Commodities and Medicines. They earnestly appeal to all those interested in the work of this Association to accord them generous support in the coming year so that no branch of the work may have to be discontinued through lack of funds.

The Committee again thanks Mr Buckham W. Liddell for his services as Auditor.

1919

New Matron Appointed

It is with satisfaction that the Committee have secured the services of Sister J.M. Campbell as Matron of the Nursing Home. She returned to work in the District after four years' war service under 'The French Flag'. She received the 'Croix de Guerre'. Unfortunately, owing to an accident on the ice, she has been unable to work for several months.

Owing to the change of Matron, the usual Christmas Gift Day did not take place until February 26th.

Mr and Mrs Sandeman of Fonab are kindly organising a Garden Fete and sale in their grounds on August 26th to raise funds to improve the sanitary arrangements, provide a Surgical Room, and, if possible, a Children's ward at the Nursing Home, at a probable cost of £2,000. It is hoped that the Public will give cordial support to this effort so that funds may be secured to enable the building to be begun as soon as possible.

1920

Qualified Maternity Nurse Employed

As the Pitlochry Branch of the Atholl and Pitlochry District Maternity and District Nursing Association has been dissolved, the Committee had added a Qualified Maternity Nurse to their staff – Nurse Christina Stewart – who is available primarily for whole time and District Maternity Nursing in Pitlochry area. The nurses' accommodation was at Catherine Bank, Pitlochry. Eighty-nine patients have been attended by the District Nurse, 35 school children, and 2,005 visits paid, 51 nights on duty. The Maternity Nurse has been engaged for 9 cases since January.

1921
Semi-Jubilee of Atholl Nursing Home
Dr Barbour, of Bonskeid, presiding at the semi-jubilee annual meeting of the Irvine Memorial Nursing Home for Atholl and the Pitlochry District Nursing Association, commended the valuable work done during the past 25 years over a wide district. In the additional Annual Report the president, Lady Helen Tod, mentioned that a legacy of £100 had been given to the Nursing Home under the will of the late Mrs Robertson, of Auchleeks; donations of £500 each for the endowment funds of the two branches of work carried on had been received from Mrs Butter, of Cluniemore; while Col. Butter had given a donation of £230 2s 10d to the District Nurse Endowment Fund, by a fete at Fonab. £1,176 4s 1d was raised in aid of the extension of the Nursing Home, and other donations brought the fund up to £1,372. The reports were approved, and satisfaction was expressed with the able manner in which the work of the Association was performed under the direction of Lady Helen Tod and the Committee.

Nursing Home Extension Fund
The amount at credit of the Nursing Home Extension Fund has been augmented by the proceeds of a very successful Jumble Sale and Christmas Fair held in Pitlochry on December 10th, which realised £337 10s 1d – making the existing deposit in the Bank, and with interest thereon, a total of £1,817 7s 3d.

1922
Closed for Alterations – 15th June 1922
For the first time since it was built, 25 years ago, the Irvine Memorial Nursing Home at Pitlochry has been closed to allow of the alterations connected with the provision of an operating theatre being proceeded with. It is not expected that the Home will be closed for more than four weeks.

Nursing Home Re-opened
The Committee of Management beg to report that the Nursing Home was re-opened for patients in October after being closed for 4 months for alterations and improvements, and in March the new Operating Room and other accessories were completed. Gift Day on that occasion was highly successful – 115 parcels of Groceries, &c., being received, and £24 14s 6d in money, which sum has been retained to purchase hospital linen and small items of furnishing. Other gifts include an Operating Table, Trolley, and furnishings for the Operating Room.

It is with deep regret that the Committee record the death of Nurse Christina Stewart. She had, by her kind and gentle services, endeared herself to the patients during the year and a half that she was in charge of the Maternity and Child Welfare Branch of the District Nursing.

1923

22nd March 1923 – Atholl Nursing Home Extension
The Irvine Memorial Nursing Home for Atholl, at Pitlochry, erected in 1902 as a memorial to the late Dr W.S. Irvine, has had its facilities greatly added to by the provision of an operating theatre with additional accommodation for the staff and other offices, at a cost of about £2,650, towards which the sum of £1,940 has been raised. The new building was formally opened yesterday by Mr Hugh Mitchell, F.S.A., convener of the Building Committee, who mentioned that it been fully furnished through the kindness of friends of the Home including Mrs Small Pender of Dirnanean, Dr W.M. Biden, Perth Red Cross Society, and Fonab Red Cross Hospital. The Home serves three large parishes, Blair Atholl, Moulin and Logierait.

1924

1st January 1924 – Women's Guild Donation
Logierait Parish Church Women's Guild have allocated the proceeds of the last Guild sale to the church restoration fund, organ fund, foreign and home missions, Christmas treat to children, Quarrier's Homes, Edinburgh; Royal Infirmary, Irvine; Memorial Home, Pitlochry; and Deaconess Hospital, Edinburgh.

1925

District Nurse Accommodation

As the funds for the upkeep of the District Nurse are low, the Committee have for some time been desirous to find accommodation for her at a lower outlay. They have now secured from the Highland District Committee of the County Council a steel unfurnished house at a rental of £23 per annum. The CO and officers of the 112th Company Glasgow Boys Brigade have most kindly promised to give the proceeds of their concert in the Pitlochry Public Hall on July 17th towards the furnishing of the Nurses Home.

Pitlochry Town Hall.

6th August 1925 – Gift to Atholl Home

Presiding at the annual meeting of subscribers to the District Nursing Association and Irvine Memorial Nursing Home at Pitlochry, Mrs Dewhurst*, Tom-na-Monachan, intimated the inauguration of the Beatrice Stewart of Strathgarry, Killiecrankie, and her brothers and sisters, with a donation of £500. The object of the fund is to enable deserving cases in the district to have the benefit of the skill of first-class surgeons for operations in the District Nursing Home.

*Mrs Dewhurst was the wife of Commander Harry Dewhurst of the cotton manufacturers, who had bought Tom-na-Monachan, once Miss Emma Molyneux's home.

1926

Annual Report

During the year ending 30th June, 84 patients have been received into the Nursing Home for treatment – 40 male, 44 female; 40 medical, 44 surgical. Four operations have been performed by surgeons from Edinburgh and 4 by Dundee surgeons; 15 by local doctors. Three cases have received assistance from the Beatrice Stewart Fund. Three discharged soldiers have occupied the Untied Services bed and 4 dependents of ex-servicemen.

In order to help defray the unexpected cost of putting the drains in order at the Nursing Home, Mrs Dewhurst proposes to hold a Garden Party on Thursday 18th August at Tom-na-Monachan. She has asked the clergy in the district served by the Home if they will combine with her by having a collection in Church on Sunday, 21st August, so making it a local 'Hospital Sunday'. Mrs. Dewhurst sincerely hopes that all interested in the Nursing Home will make a special effort to come to the Garden Party.

1927

Garden Fete and Donations

As a result of the Garden Fete held at Tom-na-Monachan through the kindness of Comm. And Mrs. Dewhurst, the handsome sum of £155 10s was handed over by them, which included collections from the churches in the district.

...putting the drains at the Home in proper order. When this expense was met, and also that of some minor alterations at the Home, there was a surplus which has been allocated to the Road Fund. The purpose of this Fund is for the repair of the Nursing Home Road. The Committee of Management arranged with the Highland District Committee of the County Council to have the work completed this summer. Mr Duff kindly gave a portion of his garden property so that the awkward corner at the entrance to the Nursing Home road might be rounded off.

The Pitlochry Branch of the WRI gave £5 for the upkeep of the wireless set and the Committee beg to thank them for their kindness.

1928

20th July 1928 – Perthshire Laird's Generous Gifts

Mr James Duff of Glenericht, Blairgowrie and Glasgow, has gifted £1,000 to the Irvine Memorial Home, Pitlochry, in memory of his father and mother; £1,000 to Strathardle and Glenshee Nursing Association in memory of his wife; and £1,000 to Blairgowrie and Rattray Cottage Hospital in memory of his only son, Alister, who fell at Gallipoli. In each case the sum is to be treated as capital, and the annual income used for the general purposes of each institution.

Annual Report

Twenty-one accidents were admitted. The increasing frequency of motor accidents is adding to the financial responsibilities of the Home.

The District Nurses attended 240 cases, 179 medical, 56 surgical, five maternity, and paid 2,545 visits, 808 Public Health visits, a total of 3,353 visits.

Miss MacGregor Stewart resigned from the post of Matron as from January 1929 and the good wishes of the Committee go with her to Craigroyston, which she has opened as a Convalescent Home.

30th October 1928 – Pitlochry Banker's Bequests

Public bequests amounting to £5,900 have been made under the will of Mr Hugh Mitchell, FSA, for 54 years solicitor and banker at Pitlochry, whose death occurred on 17th October, at the age of 75 years, as follows:

£3,000 to the Irvine Memorial Nursing Home for Atholl, £2,000 to be held by the Trustees as part of the Endowment Fund, and the balance may be expended from time to time in enlarging and improving the home.

£1,000 to the Pitlochry Established Church, to be applied towards the maintenance of the services, and in augmentation of the stipend of the minister for the time being.

£100 to the Church of Scotland Home Missions.

£1,000 to Foreign Missions.

£200 to the Aged and Infirm Ministers' Fund.

£500 to the Church of Scotland General Trustees, as a contribution
to the funds for the management of the property.

£100 to Edinburgh Royal Infirmary.

1930

16th April 1930 – Irvine Memorial Nursing Home, Pitlochry

The COMMITTEE invite applications to tender for the BRICK, JOINER,
SLATER, and ROUGH CAST, PLUMBER and PLASTER WORKS of the
Proposed Alterations and Extensions to Existing Buildings.

Plans may be seen at the Home or the Architect's Office.

The Committee reserve the right to restrict or select from the List of
Applications received. Contractors should submit applications not later
than 19th April 1930.

Tenders to be lodged with the Architects on or before WEDNESDAY,
the 30th April 1930.

The Lowest or any Offer may not be accepted.

JOHN BURNET, SON & DICK, Architects

239 St Vincent Street, Glasgow, G2.

11th August 1930 – Satisfactory Nursing Funds at Pitlochry

The annual meeting of subscribers of Irvine Memorial Nursing Home,
Pitlochry, and Pitlochry Nursing Association was held in the Lesser
Hall, Pitlochry on Saturday afternoon.

In connection with the improvement scheme at Irvine Home,
estimated to cost £3,450, it was reported that the cost was being met
largely by legacy of £500 from the late Mr Alistair C. Sandeman of Fonab,
£1,000 from the late Mr Hugh Mitchell, a donation of £1,000 from Mrs
Sandeman in memory of her husband, and other donations.

During the year, 96 patients had been admitted into the home.
District Nurse Dow was in attendance on 216 cases, involving 2,857
visits, and 735 public health visits. Mrs Macdonald and Mr Chas. Stewart
were thanked for their work as hon. Secretary and treasurer.

The house accounts showed income to be £1,311 5s 2d and expenditure
of £1,080 3s 11d, while the Nursing Association accounts showed income
of £373 11s 8d and expenditure of £253 6s 1d.

Lord James Stewart Murray, who was presiding, moved adoption of the report. Mrs Butter, Cluniemore, seconded. The report was unanimously approved.

Mrs Foote, Donavourd, Pitlochry, and Mrs Fraser, Loch Tummel Hotel, were appointed to vacancies on the committee. A vote of thanks to the chairman was proposed by Dr Lamont, Blair Atholl.

14th October 1930 – Killiecrankie Man's Bequest – Irvine Memorial Nursing Home and Church to Benefit

The late Mr Alex. Robertson, the Inch, Killiecrankie, whose death was the result of an accident during the summer, has under his will bequeathed the sum of £75 each to the Irvine Memorial Nursing Home, Pitlochry, and St Andrews Church (formerly UF), Blair Atholl.

26th November 1930 – Atholl Nursing Home Extensions

Yesterday afternoon a reception was held at the Irvine Memorial Nursing Home for Atholl, Pitlochry, to mark the completion of an important scheme of improvements and extensions of the building, when a large number of guests were received by Lady Helen Tod, president. The interior of the building has been completely remodelled, and two new wings have been added, which provide new wards for women and children, and also improved accommodation for the staff. The estimated cost of the work was about £4,000, towards which legacies of £500 from the late Mr Alistair C. Sandeman, of Fonab, £1,000 from the late Mr Hugh Mitchell, Pitlochry, have been applied, together with a donation of £1,000 from Mrs Sandeman in memory of her husband, while other substantial donations were also received.

1931

2nd January 1931 – Whist Drive and Dance at Ballinluig – 100 Players at New Year Function

A whist drive and dance organised by Miss Dewar, Cypress Cottage, Ballinluig, representative for Mid-Atholl for the Irvine Memorial Nursing Home in Pitlochry, was held in the Territorial Army Hut at Ballinluig.

At the whist drive over 100 players participated and Mr Alexander Smith, Mill of Logierait, Ballinluig, acted as announcer at the whist drive.

Prizes Presented

The prizes were presented by Mrs Slumman, Pitnacree Cottage, and on the call of Mr Alexander Smith, she was accorded a hearty vote of thanks. At the dance which followed, 80 to 90 couples took part.

On the call of Mr Alexander Stewart, a vote of thanks was accorded to Miss Dewar, who organised the evening's entertainment.

1932

9th March 1932 – Helping Pitlochry Nursing Home –
Whist Drive and Function at Struan

A whist drive and dance took place in Struan Public Hall in aid of the Irvine Memorial Nursing Home, Pitlochry.

After expenses were paid the sum of £10 was forwarded to the secretary of the home.

1932–33

Costings Report

The Net Cost per Patient a week was £2 19s 4¼d. This was broken down in the following manner:

Nurses salary and uniforms	15s 5¼d
Household expenses, fire, and light £1 6s 4½d	
Servants wages	4s 7¼d
Medicines and appliances	1s 11½d
Rents, taxes, and insurance	2s 11d
Repairs and furnishings	5s 11½d
Printing and miscellaneous	1s 7¾d
Garden work	5½d

The number of patients at the home was 147.

1933

4th January 1933 – Ballinluig Whist Drive and Dance

A whist drive and dance organised by Miss Helen Dewar, Ballinluig, was held in the Mid-Atholl Public Hall, Ballinluig. The proceeds were in aid of the Irvine Memorial Nursing Home, Pitlochry. Mr William Cameron acted as card master over 21 tables.

Charges Raised
At this meeting it was proposed and unanimously agreed to that the charges for Private Patients at the Nursing Home should be raised as follows:

One patient in large private room	£5 per week
Two patients in large private room	£3 each per week
Small private room	£4 per week

1934

2nd January 1934 – Whist Drive and Dance
A whist drive and dance was held in Mid Atholl in aid of the Irvine Memorial Nursing Home, Pitlochry, and Mid Atholl Public Hall. It was organised by Mrs Crabbie, of Eastertyre, Mr Alexander Stewart was announcer.

On the call of Mr Alexander Stewart, Mrs Crabbie was thanked.

At the dance which followed, over 120 couples participated. Music was supplied by Cook's orchestral band from Bankfoot, the M.C. being Mr Alexander Stewart.

The refreshments department was very capably managed under the superintendence of Mrs Ross, Railway Cottages; Mrs Irvine, Mrs Campbell, Mrs Macdougall, Mrs Cunningham, Mrs MacIntosh, Mrs Stewart, Mrs Patrick, Miss Addison, Miss Cameron, Miss Menzies, and Miss Macfarlane.

On the call of Mr W.A. Macintosh, Logierait, Mrs Crabbie was thanked.

Crack Shots Meet in Perthshire – Clay Pigeon Match Open to All-comers – 140 Competitors Take Part in Ballinluig Contest
International clay pigeon shots from all over Scotland, including the Island of Harris, and the North of England, and an Irish internationalist, were among the 140 competitors who took part in the clay pigeon match, open to all-comers at Inch of Tulliemet, Ballinluig, on Saturday.

The important event was organised by Logierait Gun Club in aid of the Scottish Clay Pigeon Association international fund and the Irvine Memorial Nursing Home, Pitlochry, special operation fund, and created a record for clay pigeon shooting in Scotland.

The success of the meeting was due to the excellent organising work of Mr W. A. MacIntosh, Logierait, hon. Secretary and treasurer, whose arrangements and general conduct of the competition were appreciated by all.

The competition commenced at 10.30, and the last pigeon was shattered after 6.30 in the evening.

Congratulations

Mr G. M. Foreman of Cloquhat, Bridge of Cally, President of the Scottish Clay Pigeon Association, towards the close of the competition thanked Logierait Gun Club on the successful event. He also called for special thanks to Mr W. A. MacIntosh, Hon. Secretary and treasurer, whose work, he said, was responsible for the success of the enterprise.

Mr MacIntosh returned thanks and remarked on the great service Mr Foreman had rendered to clay shooting in Scotland.

Report and Surgical Cases

The Rev. Donald Lamont, D.D., occupied the chair and said that everyone had good cause to be thankful for such institutions as the Nursing Home and District Nursing Association. He remarked on the preponderance of surgical cases over medical cases, and referred to the excellence of the operating theatre, which was so much better than the places where famous surgeons, like Syme and Lister, performed their operations within the memory of people now living. Dr Lamont also drew attention to the need to provide a fund for operation cases and thanked those who have already supported the committee in their efforts for this purpose in the past year.

The Committee would like to draw attention to the Fete which is being held at Cluniemore on 9th August in aid of the new Operation Fund, and trust that the general public will give their whole-hearted support.

In closing this report, the Committee desire to express their sincere thanks to the Matron, Nursing and District Nurse for the untiring services they have rendered during the year. They would also take this opportunity of expressing their gratitude to Mr Liddell for his services as Auditor; also, all donors, subscribers, collectors, and those who have so kindly organised entertainments for the benefit of the Home and Nursing Association.

Lady Helen Tod, President
H. Scott, Hon. Secretary

13th August 1934 – Annual Report

Mr B. A. Macnaughton presided on Saturday at the annual meeting of subscribers to the Irvine Memorial Nursing Home for Atholl and Pitlochry District Nursing Association.

The annual report showed that 179 patients had been treated in the Home, of which 34 were accident cases. The District Nurse had attended 273 cases, involving 3,970 visits.

Regret was expressed in the death of Mrs J. E. Cowan, Lagreach, who had bequeathed £1,000 in continuation of her annual contribution of £30 towards the upkeep of a bed in the Home.

The Home accounts showed an income of £1,358 with a credit balance of £236, and the district nurse account showed an income of £403, and a credit balance of £145. In reply to a question by the chairman, who said there was some feeling on the matter, it was stated that the question as to whether the Home was not being too much used for old people, to the exclusion of medical and surgical cases, was being considered by the committee. Colonel Butter explained that no case received assistance from the special operations fund until after full consideration of the circumstances, while grants made had frequently been repaid.

The reports were adopted, and the chairman expressed appreciation of the beneficent work being carried out by the Home and the Nursing Association.

3rd December 1934 – Lady Helen Tod, Sister of the Duke of Atholl

The death took place at her residence at Tirinie, Blair Atholl, on Saturday, following a sudden seizure the previous day.

Lady Helen, who was born in 1867, was the second daughter of the seventh Duke of Atholl. She had taken a lifelong interest in church and philanthropic agencies in the Atholl district. She was a keen supporter of district nursing and had been for over 30 years the president of the Irvine Memorial Nursing Home at Pitlochry.

Lady Helen had a splendid knowledge of Gaelic, and was an ardent supporter of the work of An Comunn Gaidhealach. In 1916 she married Mr David Alexander Tod, who died about 2 years ago.

4th December 1934 – Pitlochry Pound Day

A pound day at the Irvine Memorial Nursing Home, Pitlochry, was supported by 66 donors. Their contributions included more than 300 lb. of groceries and provisions, eleven dozen eggs, two turkeys, and five sacks of potatoes, together with a sum of £2 10s.

6th August 1935 – Situations Vacant

MATRON for Irvine Memorial Nursing Home, Pitlochry; fully trained nurse, theatre, and housekeeping experience. Apply, stating age, qualifications, salary, and enclosing copies of testimonials, to Mrs Butter, Cluniemore, Pitlochry. Applications to be lodged by Monday, 12th August.

1935–6

X-ray Facilities

X-ray facilities were provided due to money left by Lady Helen Tod.

1936

1st January 1936 – Blair Atholl Whist Drive

There were 22 tables at a whist drive held in the Tilt Hotel, Blair Atholl, organised by Miss Stewart, Clachan Struan, on behalf of the Irvine Memorial Nursing Home, Pitlochry. Mr Mungo Conacher was MC and Mrs Christie presented the prizes to the following: Ladies – 1 Miss J. T. Seaton, 2 (equal) Mrs J. Stewart and Mrs R. Fergusson; consolation: Miss Jean Small. Gentlemen: 1 (equal) W. Drummond and J. Sime; consolation: J. Smith.

8th April 1936 – Mid-Atholl WRI Prize Winners

The monthly meeting of Mid-Atholl WRI was held in Mid-Atholl Public Hall, Ballinluig, Mrs MacIntosh, president, presiding. Miss Margaret Dull, secretary, read her report, which was considered satisfactory. An egg collection in aid of Irvine Memorial Nursing Home, Pitlochry, was taken per Mrs MacIntosh, Logierait.

8th August 1936 – Annual Report

At the Annual meeting of subscribers to the Irvine Memorial Nursing Home for the Atholl district and Pitlochry District Nursing Association, Legacies to the Home were reported as follows:

£480 from the late Mr Alex. Stewart, Lednaskea Cottage, Strathtay;

£247 (for the Operation Fund on behalf of necessitous cases) from the late Miss McGlashan, Fincastle Post Office;

£1,000 has also been received under the will of the late Lady Helen Tod, for 32 years president of the Association, part of which the committee propose to use for the provision of a portable X-ray apparatus.

It was reported that 123 patients had been treated in the Home, including nineteen accident cases. The district nurse had attended 262 patients, involving 2,216 visits, and have also made 1,131 visits in connection with Public Health work. The Home accounts gave an income of £1,204 16s 10d with expenditure of £1,061 0s 4d; while the District Nursing accounts showed an income of £396 7s, with expenditure of £274 13s.

13th October 1936 – Wills & Estates – £500 Bequest to Pitlochry – Irvine Memorial Nursing Home Benefits

A bequest of £500 to the Irvine Memorial Nursing Home, Pitlochry, is contained in the will of Miss Emma Molyneux, of Manor Court, Harefield, Middlesex, who died aged 86 years.

She left estate of the gross value of £108,742, with net personality of £106,699.

Miss Emma Molyneux of Manor Court, Harefield, Middlesex, a Lady of Grace of St John of Jerusalem, daughter of the late John Blayds Molyneux. Net personality £106,999; gross ... £108,742. Estate duty £21,692.

She left a number of specific bequests including a large carved panel of St George and the Dragon to the Royal Society of St George; and to her trustees two letters of Lord Nelson, directing them to present the same to some person, society or institution for preservation, stating *"I hope that it may be found possible to exhibit them in a prominent position on board Lord Nelson's ship H.M.S. Victory"*; £1,000 each to the Church Missionary Society, the Gordon Boys Home, the British & Foreign Bible Society, the Church Army, the United Kingdom Beneficent Association, the order of St John of Jerusalem in England, the London City Mission, and the Distressed Gentlefolks Association; £500 each to Society for the Propagation of the Gospel, the Irvine Memorial Nursing Home, Pitlochry, the East End London Hospital for children at Shadwell; the residue of the property for such charitable objects as the executors may think proper, but with a recommendation that they should give preference to Protestant institutions, for the rescue and education of destitute boys and girls, and especially the Gordon Boys Home.

1937

13th January 1937 – Ballinluig Whist Drive Aids Nursing Home

A whist drive and dance held in the Mid-Atholl Public Hall, Ballinluig, and organised by Mrs M'Intosh, Logierait, district representative of the Irvine Memorial Nursing Home, Pitlochry, realised a sum of £26 8s.

£13 4s was sent to the treasurer of the Irvine Memorial Nursing Home, Pitlochry, and £13 4s to the Mid-Atholl Public Hall Funds.

10th July 1937 – X-ray Department Added

An X-ray department has been added to the Irvine Memorial Nursing Home for Atholl and Pitlochry. The cost has been met out of a bequest of £1,000 made by the late Lady Helen Tod, who was for 32 years president of the Home.

1938

1st January 1938 – Ballinluig Whist Drive and Dance

A whist drive and dance organised by Mrs MacIntosh, Logierait, in aid of the Irvine Memorial Nursing Home, Pitlochry, and Mid-Atholl Public Hall, Ballinluig, was held in the hall.

29th March 1938 – Blair Atholl Aids Memorial Home

An auction bridge and whist drive was held in the Tilt Hotel, Blair Atholl, in aid of Irvine Memorial Home, Pitlochry. The sum donated was not recorded.

5th August 1938 – Work Increasing at Atholl Nursing Home

Mrs Butter, Cluniemore, presided yesterday afternoon at the annual meeting of subscribers to the Irvine Memorial Nursing Home for the Atholl district and Pitlochry District Nursing Association.

The annual report stated that 139 patients had been treated in the Home, including 35 accident cases, in addition to 89 out-patients. The provision of an X-ray department at a cost of £885 had been very successful. The District Nurse had paid 3,260 visits and attended twelve school inspections. Accounts were submitted by Mr Buckham, W. Liddell, W.S., showing credit balances as follows: Nursing Home £409 14s 2d; X-ray department £6 2s 3d; Special Operations Fund £1,026 4s 11d; and District Nursing Funds £79 5s 4d.

Mrs Butter referred to the increase in the number of operations and X-ray works, and said she felt the Committee would have to face an increase of the staff, with provision of necessary extra accommodation.

There was also remitted to the Committee a suggestion by Dr Lamont, Blair Atholl, that provision might be made for housing incurable cases, while patients were waiting transference elsewhere.

Mrs Paterson, Old Blair; Mrs Stewart-Stevens, of Balnakeilly; and Mrs Crabbie of Eastertyre were appointed to vacancies on the Committee.

1942

1st January 1942 – Perthshire Ladies' Bequests

Miss Violet Olivia Juliana Ogilvy, of Balyoukan Lodge, Pitlochry, left £40 to Irvine Memorial Nursing Home, Pitlochry.

1943

22nd February 1943 – Mid-Atholl WRI Whist and Dance

A basket whist drive and dance was held in Mid-Atholl Public Hall, Ballinluig, by the Mid-Atholl WRI in aid of Institute funds 'Wings for Victory' campaign and the Operation Fund of the Irvine Memorial Nursing Home, Pitlochry.

Prize winners were:

Ladies – 1. Miss Annie H. Campbell, 2. Miss Betty McLaren,

3. Mrs A. McPhail; Ladies' consolation Mrs John Marshall

Gentlemen – 1. George D. Campbell, 2. Nurse McDowall,

3. Alexander Stewart, Gentlemen's consolation James Duff.

Prizes were presented by Mrs W.M. Crabbie.

At the dance which followed, 130 couples danced to music supplied by Staig's Orchestra, Perth. M.C.s were Alexander Stewart, Robert M. Irvine, Ian McLaren and David Robertson.

Tea was served under the supervision of Miss M. Reid and assistants.

Special prizes were won by Archibald McLean, Billie Stewart, Miss Ruby Reid, Mr Greig, George Thomson, James Haliburton and Mrs Pozzi, Tombane.

13th March 1943 – WRI Donation

The proceeds of the basket whist drive and dance recently held by the Mid-Atholl WRI in Ballinluig Hall amounted to the sum of £43 15s 3d. It was agreed to donate £10 to the funds of Irvine Memorial Nursing Home, Pitlochry (Operation Fund) and £10 as a gift to the 'Wings for Victory' campaign.

8th July 1943 – Ballinluig Collection and Nursing Home

Ballinluig door to door collection in aid of the Irvine Memorial Nursing Home, Pitlochry, per Mrs MacIntosh, Logierait, amounted to £19 14s. The collectors were: Logierait, Mrs Margaret Duff; Ballinluig, Mrs Chalmers; Moulinearn and Pitcastle, Miss Annie Dewar; Tullymet and District, Mrs Greig.

1944

1st September 1944 – Perthshire Ladies' Bequests

Miss Catherine Mitchell, Wellwood, Pitlochry, left £200 to the Irvine Memorial Nursing Home, Pitlochry.

1945

4th April 1945 – Ballinluig Concert

Variety concert and dance was held in Mid-Atholl Public Hall, Ballinluig, in aid of Irvine Memorial Nursing Home, Pitlochry, and POW Funds. Organiser was Mrs McIntosh, Logierait, assisted by a committee.

Dance music was by Miss Lizzie Dewar, Mrs Dargie and Mrs David Whyte, and MCs were Messrs Robert Irvine and William Allan. Mrs McIntosh thanked the Chairman. The amount raised was not recorded.

1946

6th August 1946 – Maternity Block Appeal Delivered

The appeals committee connected with a proposed maternity block at Irvine Memorial Nursing Home have decided to defer raising further funds until the position under the Public Health (Scotland) Bill has been clarified.

Donors are given the option of having their money refunded or left on deposit in name of the committee.

Hospital Name Change

It was agreed that the name should be changed and that thereafter 'The Home' would be known as 'Irvine Memorial Cottage Hospital'.

1948

On 5th July 1948, the NHS came into being, and the Irvine Memorial Nursing Home had become the Irvine Memorial Cottage Hospital, although the 'Cottage' part of the name was quickly dropped.

3rd April 1948 – Management Transfer

In preparation for the handing over of the Irvine Memorial Hospital to the NHS, on 2nd April the Eastern Regional Hospital Board of Dundee approved of the grouping of hospitals in the area under boards of management. Irvine Memorial Hospital was transferred to the management of County and City of Perth General Hospital, along with the sum of £14,000; the hospitals in Board No. 5 (Perth and District Hospitals) were Perth City Hospital, Perth Smallpox Hospital, Bertha House, Perth and County Fever Hospital (Ballinluig), Strathearn Home, Strathmore Hospital, St Margaret's (Auchterarder), Crieff and District Cottage Hospital, Aberfeldy Cottage Hospital, Irvine Memorial Home (Pitlochry), Hillside Homes, Hillside Sanatorium, Blairgowrie and Rattray Cottage Hospital, Viewpark Nursing Home (Alyth), Meigle Cottage Hospital, Meiklour Maternity Home; in all 984 beds.

22nd June 1948 – From NHS 1948–1998 – 'The way it was'
NATIONAL HEALTH SERVICE
Executive Council for the Counties of Perth and Kinross

In order that everyone not in the present National Health Insurance Scheme (including the *dependents* of people already on Doctors' panel lists) may receive the services provided under the National Health Service it is necessary that they should *at once* choose a doctor by completing Form EC1, which can be obtained in Post Offices, Public Libraries, Offices of Local Executive Councils, or from the Doctor on whose list they desire to be placed. A form should be completed for each and every member of the family.

GEO. D. FRASER
Clerk to the Executive Council
62 Tay Street, Perth
22nd June 1948

6th July 1948 – Hospital Services Recognised
Mrs Butter, Cluniemore presided at the final meeting of the management committee of Irvine Memorial Cottage Hospital, Pitlochry, before take-over for the Ministry of Health.

On behalf of the committee, Miss C. Fergusson, Ivybank, presented Mr A. G. Marshall, Seebpore, with a leather despatch case in recognition of his services as secretary and treasurer for six years.

Miss Howie, Matron, Sister Dott and members of the staff were thanked by Mrs Butter for their devoted services, as were all who had assisted in any way.

The committee were afterwards entertained to tea by Miss Howie.

1952
9th January 1952 – Hospital News by Hand-out
The new board of management for the County and City of Perth General Hospital decided at their first sitting on Monday to exclude the press from their meetings. This decision, taken in private, was carried by 19 votes to 3.

It was stated by Mr Stiven, the secretary, there was no objection to the press, but it was felt that, because of the personal aspect of the hospital service, it would be better if the meetings were held in private. A report of the meetings will be issued to the press the following day._

(Shutting out the reporters is shutting out the ratepayers.)

Lord Provost Sir John Ure Primrose was unanimously elected chairman and Dr D. J. McLeish, former chairman of the Bridge of Earn Board was appointed vice-chairman._

The following accommodation (daily) has been approved by the Scottish Secretary:

Irvine Memorial Hospital   36s 2d

Aberfeldy Cottage Hospital 37s 2d

Of all the hospitals included from Perth Infirmary to Auchterarder, Aberfeldy was the most expensive, followed by Irvine Memorial Hospital.

2nd June 1952 – Contracts, Tenders, &c

Board of Management for City and County of Perth General Hospitals – solid fuel contract. Requested tenders to supply all hospitals under their management.

14th August 1952 – Electrical Installation

Tenders requested by Board of management for Perthshire General Hospitals for Electrical Installation at the Irvine Memorial Hospital. Tenders to Ramsay and Primrose, Consulting Engineers, 172 Pitt Street (North), Glasgow.

1954

18th May 1954 – Food Contracts for Cottage Hospitals

Tenders are invited for the supply of Groceries, Provisions, Butcher meat, Bread, Teabread & Cakes, T. T. milk; and Potatoes, Vegetables. Applications to Group Secretary & Treasurer, Royal Infirmary, Perth.

1955

Burgh of Pitlochry – Irvine Memorial Hospital Facilities

Statistics were received from the Hospital Board regarding admissions to the various hospitals from the Parishes forming what might be described as the Pitlochry and Aberfeldy Areas.

	Irvine Memorial Hospital	Aberfeldy Cottage Hospital
1952	169	342
1953	119	315
1954	129	328
1955	101	356

The above include the totals for the Parishes of Moulin, Blair Atholl and Logierait. The admissions indicate that the Hospitals were well used.

9th January 1955 – Former Matron Dies in Hospital

Miss Jean McGibbon Campbell, one of the first Matrons of Irvine Memorial Hospital, Pitlochry, has died there. She was 70.

Born in Glasgow, Miss Campbell became district nurse in Pitlochry in 1912.

In the First World War, she volunteered for nursing in France and was awarded the Croix de Guerre.

After nursing in America, Miss Campbell went to St Albans. She left there a fortnight ago to retire in Pitlochry. She was taken ill in the train coming north and spent that fortnight in the nursing home where she trained.

6th June 1955 – Tenders for Fuel Contract

Board of Management for the County and City of Perth General Hospitals request Tenders for Solid Fuel Contract.

Applications to: Group Secretary & Treasurer, Royal Infirmary, Perth.

Mid to Late 1950s

Possibly 1957 – Accommodation for Nurses at IMH

It has been said that the above hospital is too small to be an economic unit and that the nurses' accommodation is inadequate for present day staffs. It would appear that both these objections could be readily overcome if an Administrative Block, etc, were provided, and local observers find it hard to understand why the Hospital Board has not acquired the Baptist Church Manse adjoining the present hospital for this purpose. The funds handed over to the Hospital Board would appear to be more than adequate to cover such a conversion. Again, the question is sometimes asked – what is the Hospital Board going to do with the money gathered for local people for the purpose of improving the hospital.

Maternity Cases

All local maternity cases are sent to Aberfeldy or Perth, a somewhat frightening prospect for the expectant mother and one which must cause much uncertainty and worry. The complete lack of maternity facilities in the town is a serious disadvantage, and if the facilities available in Pitlochry are not to be used for any other purpose, then surely here is an opportunity for the Hospital Board to rectify a grave omission. The population of Pitlochry, Blair Atholl and Ballinluig and the smaller communities of the surrounding district must number nearly 7,000, and it seems inconceivable that the nearest Maternity Hospital is at Aberfeldy, which may be as far distant as 30 miles from the patient. The establishment of a centre at Pitlochry could cut this mileage down to a reasonable figure and, in fact, would mean that most of the patients would only require to travel a mile or two. In this, as in other matters, the outlook of the patient and his or her relatives seems to be entirely forgotten.

The Irvine Memorial Hospital up to the time of nationalisation was a thriving Institution serving the needs of the people of this district in a highly satisfactory manner.

Operations and treatment were regularly carried out with considerable success and the number of patients benefitting from its facilities was quite high. In addition, the general cost of running the establishment was met by voluntary contributions, these being sufficient to meet the day to day expenses and to create a balance available for the possible extension and improvement of the building. In other words, the Hospital was in a very healthy state when handed over to the Hospital Board, the funds going with it being something like £14,000.

Today (late 1950s) the picture is entirely changed. Most local cases of illness are dealt with either in Perth or Bridge of Earn and operations simply do not now take place at Irvine Memorial Hospital. In general, it would appear, from the point of view of the local residents, the hospital has simply become a clinic where patients may be interviewed by consultants and that everything possible is being done to strangle its former activities. The result of this is that local people are now required to travel considerable distances for treatment, involving an uncomfortable journey in an ambulance which, in the case of patients who are seriously ill, could have very serious consequences (this was before the days of the new A9). It is realised that the Hospital Board is not responsible for the ambulance services, but at the same time, it is the Hospital Board arrangements which made the Ambulance service necessary. Apart, however, from the discomfort which the patients may suffer in being conveyed to hospital, much discomfort and indeed hardship is suffered by relatives residing locally who naturally desire to visit the patient. The journey from Pitlochry to Bridge of Earn, for example, leaves much to be desired and it is particularly galling to local residents to find that all this is happening while little use is made of the local hospital. The general impression created in the minds of the local people is that the human being has ceased to count in the question of Hospital Administration, and that nowadays the wish for centralisation has completely clouded the fact that patients and their relatives are pre-eminently human.

The fact that this area is rather remote and unlike other areas seems to be overlooked and, while it is true that the journey from Pitlochry to Perth is one of 30 miles over winding roads, many patients from this area are involved in much longer journeys over roads worse than the main road.

Much is said these days of the depopulation of the Highlands and there is no doubting the fact that depopulation is going on and must be resisted.

The policy of centralisation, however, encourages the drift to the towns and it is contended that the re-establishment of a reasonable Hospital service for the area at Pitlochry would help to counter the drift.

Tonsil Cases
A number of parents here complain of the fact that their children are sent away for surgical treatment of tonsils. This has always been understood by laymen to be a relatively minor operation and it is, therefore, with amazement and displeasure that parents find it is nowadays considered necessary to remove the children to some other

Hospital when, in fact, before nationalisation, all such operations were carried out locally. Much of the local criticism directed at the Hospital Administration arises from this fact alone, for the new arrangements invariably involves the parents in awkward attempts to visit the child, and it is useless to reply that there is no need for such a visit. Again, the human factor seems to have been forgotten and centralisation permitted to over-rule the natural feelings of parents.

14th February 1957 – Letter from Town Clerk of Pitlochry

GA/20   14th. February 1957.
WAS/MS.
W. M. Stevens, Esq,
Group Secretary & Treasurer,
Board of Management for the County & City of Perth General Hospitals,
Perth Royal Infirmary,
Perth.

Dear Mr Stevens,
Hospital Facilities in Pitlochry

At a meeting of the Town Council held the other evening I reported that I had received from you the statistics relating to the admissions relating to the various Hospitals and the Council asked me to report on them to a Special meeting to be held later on.

The opportunity was taken, however, to raise various matters with the funds that went to the Irvine Memorial Hospital when it was taken over by the Hospital Boards, and, while I did my best to explain what happened to the Endowment Funds, I did not seem to meet with much success.

I write, therefore, to enquire if you would be good enough to write to me and give me the following information:

1. The amount of funds passed over to the Board in respect of the Irvine Memorial Hospital (locally said to be £14,000).
2. What has happened to these funds now?
3. Are they part of the sum now emerged as the Endowment

Funds for your Board, of which it was recently decided a considerable amount should be spent on improvements at various Hospitals in Perthshire?

I regret troubling you in the matter, but it would be most helpful to me if you could write me an explanatory letter.

Yours faithfully,

Town Clerk.

(The reply from the Board of Management for the County & City of Perth General Hospitals has not be found.)

1958

General Information from 1958

In 1958 a District Nurse was employed by the County Council, and was previously employed by the District Nursing Association, was stationed in Pitlochry.

In 1958, the Sanitary Inspector for the Highland Division of Perthshire also had his office in Pitlochry.

1960s

Unfortunately, the author has been unable to find any information for this decade.

1975

4th March 1975 – Gift to help Save A9 Victims

The rise in the cost of petrol has resulted in fewer accidents on one of the most notorious roads in Scotland – Perthshire's A9.

This was said yesterday by a Pitlochry doctor who, together with the three other members in his group practice, deals with the 40-mile A9 'patch' from Dowally to Dalnaspidal, and from Enochdhu to Tummel Bridge.

Dr R. T. A. Ross made this comment at Fisher's Hotel as he accepted a cheque for £400 from Pitlochry & District Round Table which will go towards the purchase of resuscitation equipment for emergency use at A9 and other accidents.

"Out of our whole area", said Dr Ross, *"the A9 accounts for 90 per cent of the casualties"*.

Before the sharp fuel increases, the peak accident rate on the A9 averaged out at two every three days, with a staggering death toll of one a month. *"Last year was the first year the figures did not go up"*, said Dr Ross.

The cheque was handed over by Hamish Seaton of the local Round Table. Said Dr Ross: *"One wishes the need wasn't there and that the equipment won't have to be used".*

About or in the same year, 1975, a two-way radio telephone system was purchased through fund-raising and then installed.

In 1977, Ruby Ripley took up the post of Matron of the Irvine Memorial Hospital.

1979

Constitution is Set Up for Irvine Memorial

More than 100 people from Pitlochry and district attended a public meeting in Scotland's Hotel, Pitlochry, to consider a proposed constitution for the Friends of Irvine Memorial Hospital.

A local solicitor, who guided the meeting through the clauses, acknowledged the advice from the Scottish League of Friends of Hospitals, Tayside Health Board, and the existing committee.

After several minor changes, the meeting approved the constitution which states that the object of the Friends of Irvine Memorial Hospital is to promote the welfare of patients and support the work of the hospital.

The financial statement presented by Mrs Margo Ross showed that income for the year included a legacy of £1,000 from the late Mrs Jessie Dryden, a former nurse at the hospital and latterly a patient.

Retiring *en bloc*, the committee, including chairman Mrs Ross who had served since the beginning in 1974, were warmly thanked on the call of Mrs Preston-Thomas.

Mrs Ripley, matron, presented a bouquet to Mrs Ross.

Mrs Ripley and Hon. President Mrs Butter both referred to the generous support for the hospital from Pitlochry and neighbouring places.

The relationship between community and the hospital was extraordinary, and the new committee was wished every success. A new committee was appointed.

1980

Pitlochry Heart Machine Triumph

The People of Pitlochry were last night praised for an example of community effort which has resulted in the provision of a defibrillator machine for cardiac treatment by local doctors.

January 1980. Presentation of a defibrillator machine,
the money for which was raised through community efforts.
FROM LEFT: Dr D. Cruikshank, Matron R. Ripley, Dr M. Faulds,
Dr T. Ross, Dr C. Grant, Mr E. Penker (president, Vale of Atholl Pipe Band),
Mr G. Stewart & Mrs W. Sherriffs (Fund Raising Committee),
Mr I. Duncan (Pipe Major), Sister G. Proudfoot, Mr J. Stewart
(Convenor, Fund Raising Committee).
[from the Perthshire Advertiser]

Dr Christopher Grant said it was a splendid example of self-help in days when so many people sit back and wait for things to be given them.

At a ceremony in the Irvine Memorial Hospital, Dr Grant formally accepted the machine from Mrs William Sheriffs, secretary of the fund-raising committee.

Matron Ruby Ripley and some of her staff, 1979–1980.

Congratulating to all those involved on their achievement, he said his colleagues were most grateful. He revealed it had been put into operation only hours after being delivered a few days ago.

Time Vital

He also said that to have such a machine based in Pitlochry would be of tremendous benefit to the community because minutes could be vital.

He went on to recall the Sunday show last August which had given the funds a flying start of £800, and thanked the Vale of Atholl Pipe Band, all the artistes and others who helped.

Demonstration

He thanked too, everyone who contributed to the fund which closed yesterday at £2,068.

Two of the local GPs demonstrated the machine at work.

Also present at the ceremony were Dr Trevor Ross and Dr David Cruikshank, Matron Ruby Ripley, Sister Gladys Proudfoot, Mr James

Stewart and Mr George Stewart, convener, and treasurer of the fund-raising committee.

Mr Erhard Penker and Mr Ian Duncan, president, and pipe major of the Vale of Atholl Pipe Band, were also there.

Mr Bill Sutherland, of the fund-raising committee, was unavoidably absent.

22nd August 1980 – Health Service Journal –
'A Place in the Country that is not Entirely Countrified'

They built a monument to the venerable Dr William Irvine, and they called it Irvine Memorial Hospital. Eighty years on, it lives up to his good name. There is no call to rusticate at this haven of healing in, Scotland's tourist belt. Life is not all a summer idyll, as Nick Davidson discovered.

It is a steep climb to Irvine Memorial Hospital through a belt of bungalows and villas, but the views are spectacular; wooded and moorland hillsides reaching to the far horizon where earth and sky blend in a pale haze.

The 23-bed hospital is a turn-of-the-century functional building. It has been added to and now sits cramped on a piece of land it has outgrown. It serves Pitlochry and the surrounding countryside – one of Scotland's main tourist routes and an all-season wildlife and sporting centre.

Ruby Ripley, the nursing officer in charge, has a large office at the back overlooking the golf course and the mysteriously named Pitlochry Hydro Hotel, a solid Victorian building with tenuous links with either water or spas.

"When I moved here from a 650-bed hospital in East Kilbride, all my friends said I was going to rusticate", she said with a gleeful grin, *"but I've done more types of acute work here than I would even have seen there. I've been here three years and I've had more satisfaction than in the previous ten put together"*.

She likes the area – so do hundreds of other people, which is why it has become a retirement area – but above all she has become a fervent convert to cottage hospitals. *"I couldn't have imagined what it was like before I came. I used to be a full-time nursing administrator without any patient contact. This job is meant to be a full-time administrative post, but I'm in contact with staff and patients all the time. I like it that way; there is no divide because I'm the nursing officer and nursing auxiliary; in that way we also give a higher standard of nursing."*

Money is not a headache

"Staff morale is correspondingly high. We have a very low sick list", maintained Mrs Ripley. *"We don't have half-days off with headaches and we do have people coming in when they are quite unwell. In my previous job it was routine to check up every day on who wasn't in rather than who was."*

The hospital enjoys other advantages which probably rub off on staff. By a fortunate quirk of fate, it is not short of money. It has been scheduled for upgrading. *"I can't honestly say we are feeling the pinch at all"*, said Mrs Ripley as she escorted me around a disorganised kitchen in the process of being redesigned and refitted. *"That hot cabinet is a bit big, though, isn't it"*, she added, as we squeezed past the cook, a local farmer's wife who had come in because the full-time cook was away. *"We'll have to see if we can't get that changed."*

The hospital is also benefiting from a recent decision by Tayside Health Board not only to maintain its small hospitals – the last talk of closure was in the early '70s – but to expand them. The Irvine Memorial, in common with several others in the surrounding area, has got a new geriatric unit. It is a spacious and generous mixture of single and four -bedded· wards – twelve beds in all – that has gobbled up the last piece of, garden. The unit is a standard design that could be trimmed· and reduced in size by future economies. The hospital feels fortunate to have got it just in time.

"Isn't it lovely", said Mrs Ripley, as we pushed our way through builder's rubble blocking the corridor. *"There's only one serious mistake. That's in this bathroom, where somebody has repositioned the bath at the last moment. It's impossible to stand up in it without cracking your head on the roof beam. That'll have to be moved."* The clean, spacious, sunlit rooms look a better place than most to spend your last days, if you have to spend them in hospital, and it will save the elderly of the district, not to mention their relatives, a 30-mile trek to Perth to the nearest alternative geriatric beds.

Informal league of supporters

The hospital also enjoys, like most small hospitals, enormous community support. It does not have a formal league of friends, but the five-strong Friends of the Irvine Memorial Hospital – three doctors' wives and the heads or the local Red Cross and WRVS – fulfils the same role. Audrey Grant, wife of one of the hospital's four GPs and member of the Friends, said: *"When the new geriatric unit opens there may be a need for the kind of service a league of friends can provide, but we haven't needed it until now. We· provide the odds and ends the health board doesn't: a toaster for the nurses; a hostess trolley; little extras you can't get through the health service".*

She is perhaps a little self-effacing. *"Don't listen to her"*, said Mrs Ripley as Mrs Grant left the room to go and man her husband's switchboard. *"She does a tremendous amount."*

Notwithstanding the power of Dr Irvine's name, or the continued support of the community, the hospital has problems that are shared by many small hospitals. It is in a rural area, 30 miles from the parent DGH in Perth. Supplies can often cost more in transport costs than the items themselves are worth. Oxygen, for instance, used to come from Dundee and the transport cost more than the oxygen itself. The hospital recently switched to taking supplies from the district pharmacy and is saving about £800 each year.

Distance can be a strain

The four GPs cover enormous distances and are often not immediately available, which can put strains on nursing staff. *"You have got to be able to use your own initiative"*, said Sister Celia Talbot. *"You have got to be able to assess a casualty (the hospital deals with about 2,500 casualty patients every year, the summer months being particularly busy) and take it on yourself to do something. You have got to be able to decide very quickly what you can cope with and what you cannot."*

The hospital has been progressively shorn of the services it can offer. There used to be fairly major surgery until the late '50s, but Tayside Health Board policy has changed and there is now only minor surgery – toe nails, warts, etc. Consultants do, however, offer most of the usual outpatient clinics.

Staff have meanwhile had to fight hard to maintain a regular throughput of patients to ensure that beds do not get blocked by elderly patients. It has been largely successful. It has managed to keep long-stay patients down to about two and it is hoped that the new geriatric unit will clear these.

Lunch was being served as I left. A couple of elderly patients had been wheeled into the drawing-room. Outside a man was playing golf. It was a peaceful scene. A nice place to visit and, by universal assent, a nice place in which to work and live.

Some Information on the Running of Irvine Memorial Hospital
1. When a patient is returning to a Sheltered Housing Complex or a Residential Home the Warden/Officer-in-Charge is contacted.
2. If transport by ambulance is required, this is organised and a suitable time agreed.
3. If special 'Aids to Daily Living' are required, in conjunction with the Social Work Department, the Community O.T. is contacted and a visit to the patient's home is organised and the necessary equipment is provided by their department.

Out-Patient Department and Accident & Emergency Department

Situated to the right of main entrance. Well signposted.
Emergency admissions are normally brought in via the front entrance.
Internal access to Outpatient Department & Accident & Emergency is off main corridor – GP Unit.

CLINICS ARE HELD ON A REGULAR BASIS for the following specialties:
SURGICAL – MEDICAL – ENT – GYNAECOLOGY – ORTHOPAEDICS – DIETETICS and X-RAY.
The OUT-PATIENT DEPARTMENT IS ATTACHED TO THE GP UNIT AND THE GP STAFF ARE RESPONSIBLE FOR THESE CLINICS.

Surgical Clinics: 2nd Monday and 4th Wednesday each month – Morning Clinics – Consultant – Mr. I. Davidson.

Medical Clinics: 2nd Friday – Dr W. Gray – Afternoon Clinic –
4th Monday – Dr R. Wood – Morning Clinic.

Gynaecology: 2nd Tuesday each month – Afternoon Clinic –
Consultant – Dr J. Donald.

ENT: 2nd Wednesday – Mr J. Brennand – Morning Clinic –
4th Thursday – Dr Majmudar – Morning Clinic.

Orthopaedics: Mr W. Hadden comes every two months on the
afternoon of the 4th Thursday of the month. Appointments for this
clinic are made from PERTH by Mr Hadden's secretary.

Dietic Clinic: Held on the first Monday of each month – Morning
Clinic. This Clinic also arranges own appointments and referrals
are made direct to the Department at PRI by GP.

X-Ray: Limited X-ray service provided. EVERY SECOND TUESDAY –
Appointments normally made direct from GP to patient.
HOSPITALS STAFF DO NOT SEND OUT APPOINTMENTS TO
PATIENTS FOR THIS CLINIC.

Special Facilities

Physiotherapy: two sessions (am) per week.

OT Assistant: three sessions per week – duties mainly relating to
Atholl Ward and Day Hospital patients.

Chiropody

Dental: Arrangements are made via the appropriate channels for an
In-patient service to be provided if/when necessary.

Optical: [Not on Site]

Ancillary Staff – Catering & Cleaning: Supervised on a day to day
basis by the Nursing officer or her Deputy but come under the
control of the Administration Department who are responsible for
all aspects of their employment.

Catering Arrangements: Organised at local level by Nursing Officer.
There are no special facilities provided on a formal basis for
relatives or visitors.

Hospital Policies: E.g. Fire Procedure. Care of Valuables etc. The
policies laid down by Perth & Kinross District and Tayside Health

Board are adhered to. An alphabetically documented comprehensive information book detailing guidelines relating to administration, ordering etc. is available for all staff to refer to.

Smoking: Restricted. Certain areas are designated for both patients and staff to use.

Induction Programmes: For Nursing Staff – organised by Nursing Officer and Senior Staff. For Ancillary Staff – this is the responsibility of Administrator responsible for this group of staff in conjunction with Nursing Officer.

Residential accommodation: There is a Nurses Home with limited accommodation. Staff changing· rooms are located in this area.

Shopping Trolley: Twice weekly service organised by Ladies Circle.

Newspapers: Delivered daily. The local Rotarians pay for a regular supply to the GP Unit.

A close contact is maintained with District Nursing colleagues, Ambulance Service, Social Services Department, and various other outside agencies and Voluntary Organisations.

The Friends of Irvine Memorial Hospital are a very active Group who work very hard to provide many extras.

1981

New Geriatric Unit

At Irvine Memorial Hospital, Pitlochry the new £240,000 geriatric unit has been operational since November last year and is proving extremely popular with staff and patients alike. The wing was completed in October 1980 but temporarily housed the general hospital facilities at Pitlochry while the original 1901 building was extensively up graded.

Irvine Memorial's geriatric unit also has twelve beds divided between two four-bedded wards and four single rooms. All have toilets and wash basins en-suite. Cottage hospitals have a special place in small communities and that is reflected by the generosity of people in their catchment areas.

For example, a local fund in Blair Atholl provided a special Medic bath for Irvine Memorial's new geriatric unit. Flower stands for the corridors were gifted by local people, and the youngsters of Logierait Primary School raised money to provide furniture for the day room, assisted by grants from Perth & Kinross Silver Jubilee Fund and Help the Aged.

The Pitlochry unit caters for one- or two-day patients but the beds are mainly occupied by long-stay old people. To run efficiently, hospitals must have their routine and rules. But Irvine Memorial's matron, Mrs Ruby Ripley, believes that flexibility is important, and the pictures and ornaments of the unit's patients give the building a homely atmosphere.

Irvine Memorial Hospital has facilities for medical, surgical, psychiatric, gynaecological, ear, nose & throat, and speech therapy clinics as well as X-ray and treatment room facilities. And the latter is put to good use.

Last year, the Pitlochry Hospital staff dealt with a staggering 2,174 casualties – many of them summer season visitors.

At present, Irvine Memorial Hospital has eleven practitioner beds in two for-bedded wards, one double and a single room.

Atholl Ward

At this time there was the Atholl Ward, a long-term geriatric and subsequently dementia unit.

1982

Health Service Strikes

The MP for Kinross & West Perthshire wrote about strikes:

> "The health workers are being forced, at last, to accept reality. Their strikers are another group who don't care who suffers in their cause. But I fear a dreadful legacy for all of us, apart from the thousands of 'non-emergency' patients who will have to suffer pain and disability for months or years more than they need have.
>
> The legacy, I fear, will come from the setting up of a 'Review Body'. Review bodies tell the country what a group of people would like to be paid and therefore deserve to be paid. They don't ever point out that everybody else is going to have to pay for it or where the money is coming from.
>
> We don't need a review body to point out that nurses and

doctors could be paid at least a thousand pounds a year more if private firms replaced the thousands of administration and ancillary workers, some of whom organised these disgraceful strikers.

Contrast those on the picket lines with the devoted staff of Pitlochry Cottage Hospital which I had the joy of visiting this week. The staff there from the matron to the gardener work out of a sense of devotion to their patients.

They don't moan and groan about overtime and petty-fogging differentials. They work for love, and the money is just a bonus.

Isn't it a tragedy that such a spirit, which is the quintessence of country life, can't be transferred to the shop stewards of urban communities who work for money? Love takes very much last place, and sometimes I think hate is a long way ahead of it."

Article in Comment

'COTTAGE HOSPITALS'
by Ruby Ripley

I WAS INTERESTED to read Dr McBride's article on Cottage Hospitals in the last issue of *COMMENT*. He obviously feels as I do that they serve the community very well. Eight years ago I knew very little of the Cottage Hospital set-up. One day, when scanning the sits vac column in a newspaper, I saw my present port advertised and my interest was aroused. I applied for, and after interview, was offered the position.

When I told my friends and colleagues of my plans for the future they were rather sceptical and some of their remarks were less than complimentary. The general consensus of opinion was that I would soon be bored out of my mind and would eventually rusticate. I explained to them that I needed more patient contact and this I would get in the Cottage Hospital. They have certainly been proved wrong on all counts. My work is varied and interesting. A broad based nursing experience is gained in this type of hospital and there is a great deal of job satisfaction at all levels.

Family Feeling
In a post such as this it is essential to maintain close contact with the

patients and relatives and it is also important to build up good community relationships; this, I think, has been done. One gets the feeling that we are an integral part of the local scene. Staff are most supportive and when a crisis occurs, as can happen, everyone rallies around to help. There is a feeling of 'family' and everyone appears to be happy at their work. The staff are also involved in community life and a tremendous amount of goodwill and support is apparent. We have lots of extras, benefitting both patients and staff, provided through the generosity of local people.

Donations and Support

The Friends of Irvine Memorial Hospital are friends in the true sense of the word. Many people outwith the area show their appreciation by sending donations to the Friends. Recently four lovely prints were presented by a grateful patient (a holidaymaker) in appreciation of the care, kindness and courtesy that he received when a patient here. Our patio tubs and garden furniture have all been donated by people wanting to show their appreciation. A recent visitor (president of an

Pupils of Pitlochry High School presented 'lifting belts' in 1989.

inter national bank in New York) was so impressed by the medical and nursing care that he received as an in-patient that ·he thinks 'he will call again'! To sum up, Cottage Hospitals such as ours provide a good service and are certainly good places to work. I am sure that I speak for all our staff and patients when I say: long may we continue to serve the community.

1989

25th January 1989 – Hats off to Pitlochry High's Primary 7

It's amazing how one thing leads to another, as young Pitlochry pupils have been discovering – from a sponsored clean-up to the Queen Mother's hat, for example!

It all began when the boys and girls of Primary 7 at the high School in the town decided they would like to do something to help the patients at the Irvine Memorial Hospital.

As a result of a sponsored clean-up they all went along to the hospital to present the cheque, meet some of the patients and give them gifts.

It proved to be a memorable occasion for young and old alike, and not least for 97-year old Annie Stead, who had put on her best dress for the visit and so charmed the pupils that it was decided that two of them would go back to see her as representatives of the class.

The children – Gayle Christie and Helen Hobson – were fascinated by what she had to tell them about her childhood in Huntly and working life in Dundee and later in Pitlochry hotels.

And it was then that the Queen Mother's hat came into the story – well almost!

When the girls asked her what she would most like she told them the only wish she had left was to have one of the Queen Mother's old hats!

So when Gayle and Helen went back to school, it was agreed Primary 7 would try to do a 'Jim'll fix it' for Annie.

On December 20, this letter was sent off to Clarence House:

> *"Your Majesty, The Queen Mother, We are writing this letter*
> *to you to make a special request for a happy smiling little lady of*
> *97 years old who lives in the Atholl ward of our local nursing home.*
> *Her name is Annie Stead and she told us when our class was*

111

visiting the hospital recently, that her only wish left was to own one of the Queen Mother's old hats. (She does not know that we are writing to you as we want to keep this a secret.)

Our class decided recently that we would like to raise some money to help our excellent hospital so we did a sponsored clean-up.

It was when we presented our cheque to the hospital that we met Annie Stead. She had put on a lovely dress for the occasion and we had our photographs taken in a large group of patients, matron, teacher and pupils.

We enjoyed seeing the happy faces of all the patients when they opened the parcels and cards which we gave them.

We hope you have a Happy Christmas and a peaceful New Year."

A few days later, back came a reply on behalf of the Queen Mother. It said:

"The Queen Mother was very interested to hear about Annie Stead and although it is not possible to accede to your request, Her Majesty has bidden me to send the enclosed booklet.

The Queen Mother hopes you will give it to your elderly friend and says it comes with Her Majesty's warmest good wishes.

I am also to say that Queen Elizabeth was so pleased to learn that you have all been visiting the local nursing home, and have raised funds for your hospital.

Her Majesty feels sure that this has been much appreciated by both staff and patients."

Helen and Gayle went back to visit Annie a day or two ago, and Gayle said later, *"We read the Queen Mother's letter to her and gave her the booklet and other presents."*

"I don't think she could believe her ears!"

"Annie said that she would always remember Helen and me and that she thought it was nice that some young people come to visit the old".

Presentation of a cheque from the Atholl Highlanders to
Friends of Irvine Memorial Hospital at Blair Castle, May 1991.
L to R: Peter Kemp, Ian Murray, Duke of Atholl,
Ruby Ripley and Shirly Gilchrist.

1990s

Health Service Strikes

In this year, the nursing home began to feel the strain of not being big enough for all that was required. Prior to 1979, the A9 was a two-way road from Perth to Inverness, but by 1990 after the rebuild of the A9 with some of the road made into dual carriageway, traffic was increasing, mainly in speed, causing a number of fatal crashes and many injuries. This was requiring more medical attention from the GPs at this time, only four.

The Irvine Memorial Hospital played a part in many factors.

One was immediate help for minor injuries off the A9; major injuries were taken to Perth or Ninewells [Dundee] by ambulance; the Air Ambulance was still to come.

Dr Trevor Ross of Pitlochry GP Surgery explained the situation in an interview of 4th July 1990.

Scotland's Busiest Motorway Medic

Holiday-makers are taking the high road to DEATH in Scotland.

The tourist rush has started – and casualty services on the scenic Scottish routes are bracing themselves for soaring accident statistics.

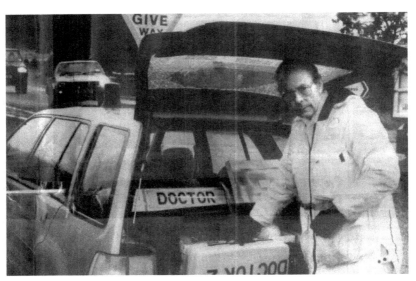

Dr Trevor Ross with Emergency Medical Vehicle, c.1990.

Notorious

It's speed that kills – and this week the Scottish Home Affairs Minister ordered a clamp-down on speedsters, who turn many of our roads into death traps.

Most notorious is the A9, a killer road to the Highlands, where drivers have been clocked at speeds as high as 155 mph!

And Dr Trevor Ross knows what it is like to be called to the sickening scenes of carnage.

For the past 22 years as a GP based in Pitlochry, part of the frontline role has been to answer emergency call-outs to horror smashes – DAY AND NIGHT!

His medical skills are often the first assistance crash victims in mangled motors receive.

Dr Ross and his three colleagues cover a 48 mile stretch of the A9 from Drumochter to just north of Dunkeld.

Unpaid

In 1989, the Tayside practice attended a staggering 84 accidents – and 12 people lost their lives. This year, 7 people have died on their patch so far, four in one accident back in January.

As a member of the British Association for Immediate Care (BASIC), Dr Ross carries out the A9 medical patrol work unpaid, in addition to his other vital activities as a busy family doctor.

BASICS involves over 2,000 doctors nationwide.

Alert

These medics provide lifesaving on the spot through resuscitation, stabilising people's conditions administering painkilling injections and being on the alert for possible complications.

Dr Ross and his colleagues can be at the scene of a crash victim within twenty minutes. His diagnosis for the death toll and number of crashes on the A9 is:

1.	Drivers going too fast
2.	'Loony' overtaking
3.	Bumper to bumper driving.

Dr Ross is also convinced the 282-mile-long road is plagued by bad junctions, single carriageway bottlenecks and dangerously-positioned signposts.

Fatalities

Dr Ross said the new road had NOT reduced the number of fatalities, and on his patch, they were continuing to run at about a dozen a year.

Only hours after a new booklet was launched aimed at improving its safety standards, the road claimed another life.

The victim was driving a car which collided with a lorry near the village of Ballinluig, twenty miles north of Perth, within Dr Ross's area. The car rolled several times after the impact and ended up on its roof.

Died

The driver died from his injuries in Perth Royal Infirmary.

As Dr Ross and his partners get set for another summer of emergency dashes to accident blackspots in their specially equipped estate cars, he hit out at the planners.

He criticises them for rarely seeking advice of medical men such as himself. He blasted: *"Maybe if they sat in the middle of the road at a crash scene with the blood of a victim running through their fingers, they would pay more attention!"*

Dr Ross retired in 2005 and died in 2009.

Call-outs were often and the hospital taking in casualties when more serious or major medical attention was not required, plus holiday-makers becoming unwell or injuring themselves, the clinics were busy with local appointments. However, one idea which came forward was to build a therapeutic garden to allow in good weather the ward patients to go outside into a peaceful garden where the local schoolchildren volunteered to come and help maintain the garden.

To obtain the garden a great deal of negotiation took place throughout the next few years to acquire land from an adjoining property and the altering of walls and the layout of the garden in which there was to be a lily pond, a shrub bed with a bird table, raised beds and a pergola, plus flower beds.

During this period, the Friends of Irvine Memorial Hospital were busy supplying medical equipment, soft furnishings, kitchen equipment, arts & crafts materials, and social outings, plus providing financial help for the community extension.

By 1990, a community extension was added; this area provided a number of extra patient facilities. A large part of the cost was met by funding from the Friends of Irvine Memorial Hospital, by which time the Friends had a Constitution. They had provided:

A hairdressing room,

Maintenance of the garden

Contributing towards the building of the Community Room
Spenco and air cell mattresses
Specialised baths
ECG and other specialised equipment
Defibrillator
Equipment for Out-patient and A&E departments
Equipment for Occupational Therapy and Physiotherapy
Provision of televisions, video recorders, music centre and
electronic organ
Provision of many varied items of furniture, including reclining
and therapeutic chairs.

On 29th May 1996 the Therapeutic Garden at Irvine Memorial
Hospital, Pitlochry, was officially handed over to Irvine Memorial
Hospital by Major Sir David Butter KCVO, MC, from the Friends of
Irvine Memorial Hospital. The official ceremony at 12 noon was:

Welcome by Mr J. M. Mathieson OBE, DL, JP
Opening by Major Sir David Butter KCVO, MC
Dedication by Rev W. Shannon
Vote of thanks by Mr J. M. Mathieson OBE, DL,
JP Photographic Opportunity
A Buffet Lunch was provided.

The concept of establishing a garden for the Hospital was first mooted
in 1991 by the then Chairman of the Hospital's League of Friends, who
suggested that a piece of ground belonging to the adjacent Castlebeigh
Hotel might be acquired for the purpose. An approach to the hotel's
owners was received sympathetically and the land purchased in 1993 by
the then Perth & Kinross Unit of Tayside Health Board (later Perth &
Kinross Health Care NHS Trust). The League of Friends undertook to
bear the cost of landscaping and upkeep.

A garden committee was set up comprising a local GP, Mr Affleck
Gray, a well-known landscape gardener and author, and two HNS
representatives.

Garden plans were drawn up. The emphasis was on low maintenance, with a large paved area including seating for patients and relatives, a moving water feature, and raised beds to enable patients to benefit from the therapeutic value of involvement in gardening. A summer house and greenhouse were added subsequently.

Although the hard landscaping was contracted out, much of the credit for the quality of the garden must go to the late Mr Affleck Gray and Willie Christie, who put in more than their share of labour in planning and planting out shrubberies and borders. Affleck Gray not only made regular visits to make the garden bloom, but was closely involved with local schoolchildren on their regular visits, turning the garden into a place where old and young could work together.

The cost of the project totalled £25,000, £10,000 for the land from the NHS and £15,000 from the League of Friends for landscaping, planting, and structures.

Perth & Kinross Health Care NHS Trust chairman Mr John Mathieson sees the garden as indicative of the close involvement which typifies the community hospitals in Perthshire. *"This part of the world is fortunate in having a string of excellent small hospitals to provide a service which complements the specialist services at PRI. Much credit for the friendly atmosphere in these hospitals must go to the Leagues of Friends who make sure that there is a distinctively local flavour to the place, and this splendid garden demonstrates their commitment for patients, staff and visitors alike."*

By the late 1990s, unrest was coming to the Pitlochry area in the roles the NHS thought cottage hospitals should play. On 27th July 1998 a PUBLIC MEETING TO DISCUSS NHS REFORMS was announced to discuss the impact of NHS reforms in Highland Perthshire. Concern had been growing over the implications of the white paper 'Designed to Care', especially for the Irvine Memorial Hospital.

The organiser said around 200 locals were expected to attend to hear and question the speakers, who would include senior representatives from Perth & Kinross Health Care NHS Trust and local GPs. The North Tayside MP was also due to attend. The meeting, in the Town Hall, was sponsored by the Rotary and Probus Clubs of Pitlochry.

The response from locals was far greater than anyone could have anticipated. A letter to the papers on 3rd August described the event well:

COMMUNITY HOSPITALS THREAT

"Sir, – I attended a remarkable meeting at Pitlochry Town Hall on July 27. Ten minutes before it was due to start the Hall was full and many people were turned away to ensure the meeting did not breach fire safety regulations.

At a conservative estimate it seems that about 50% of the adult Pitlochry population were present at the meeting. Its purpose was to discuss the proposal by Perth & Kinross Health Care NHS Trust to transfer a number of beds for patients suffering from dementia from the Murray Royal Hospital in Perth to the Irvine Memorial Hospital in Pitlochry.

That proposal, in conjunction with similar plans for the hospitals in Aberfeldy, Crieff and Blairgowrie, is blatantly designed to enable the Trust to close that Hospital completely, in a bare-faced attempt to save money without regard to the damaging effect the plan would have on patient care in local communities.

The proposal, if implemented, would "block" many of the beds at the Irvine Memorial Hospital with dementia patients.

It would by this destroy its essential role as a community hospital which, together with a highly efficient general medical practice, has served Pitlochry for as long as most of its citizens can remember.

Although the atmosphere at the meeting was remarkably restrained, it was clear that the vast majority of those present vehemently opposed the Trust's proposals. If the proposals are imposed, which seems probable, the citizens of Pitlochry who turned out in such vast numbers to object to them will feel betrayed."

The author attended this meeting. It came over as a very insulting occasion to the population of Pitlochry, as it was obvious from the beginning it had already been decided that a number of beds at the Irvine Memorial Hospital would be used for dementia patients, taking away beds from the locals in Pitlochry and surrounding areas and meaning if the few beds were in use, locals would be sent to Perth Royal Infirmary or Ninewells in Dundee.

Eventually the beds *were* handed over to dementia patients.

Staff group 1: BACK ROW FROM LEFT: Dr G. McRory, Dr D. Cruikshank, Dr J. MacHugh, Dr D. Kennedy, Dr D. Leaver.
MIDDLE: M. McIntosh, M. Whitehead, G. Irvine, R. Hubbard, M. Sheppard, K. Logan, J. MacDonald. FRONT: A. Michie, J. Thorne, J. Moore, J. Watson.

On 10th August, a letter from a retired GP in Aberfeldy was published:

"Sir, – The letter of Aug 3 will be endorsed in Aberfeldy, where our Cottage Hospital evidently faces proposals similar to that which it describes.

Already, for reasons which we find hard to understand, elderly, infirm patients from our locality are banished to distant places leaving empty beds here.

These little hospitals were originally built, and for years sustained, by local money and by local effort for local people. Are we to be denied admission to what we regard as our hospital because its beds are occupied by patients from elsewhere in need of psychiatric care? We will be told no doubt that the selling off of the fine land and buildings, opened in 1827 as Murray Royal

Staff group 2: BACK ROW FROM LEFT: C. Bridges, S. Taylor, A. Millar, L. Jones, I. Wensley, L. Brown, M. Ogilvie, S. Gledhill, A. McDonald, A. Hausrath, A. Winter, M. Hamilton. MIDDLE: S. Rae, M. Storey, S. Webster, M. Dow, G. Sharp, L.Foley. FRONT: I. Jones, K. Philbin, J. Fyfe, D. Lambert, V. Barr.

Asylum, thanks to the vision and altruism of James Murray, represents progress in the care of the mentally ill.

Murray's fortune, miraculously inherited, was on his death bequeathed to trustees David Beatson and Robert Peddie; both served on Perth Town Council and diligently carried out Murray's instructions that most of the money should be used to build an asylum for the benefit of mentally ill dwelling in Perth and District.

The Murray Royal thus became one of the Royal Asylums built in Scotland in the early years of the last century to promote humane treatment of the mentally ill.

These were not all grim Victorian institutions. A small booklet written in 1927 by the late Dr W D Chambers to celebrate the centenary of the Murray Royal praises the regime of care, freedom and recreation enjoyed by patients in this lovely setting.

The Irvine Memorial Hospital Garden in winter, 2002.

Can we now dispense with such a hospital? Will demented patients be happier locked in a Cottage Hospital?"

2002

Centenary Celebrations

Prior to 14th July 2002, when Centenary Celebrations for the IMH were in progress, all was put on hold for the friends and family of Miss I. Kennedy who was a patient in the Hospital to celebrate her 100th birthday. Miss Kennedy, a well-known Pitlochry resident, was born just two months before the Nursing Home was officially opened on 14th July 1902. As a child, Miss Kennedy lived on Nursing Home Brae, and remembers the new Irvine Memorial Nursing Home sitting at the top of the hill, with fields and broom-covered rough ground around it. There was a path up the brae, with a wicker gate off, into the grounds of the little two-bedded Nursing Home. Over the years, Miss Kennedy has been witness to the many developments of IMH. All were delighted to wish Miss Kennedy a happy 100th birthday, and we now look forward to marking the Centenary of IMH.

14th July 2002 – Irvine Memorial Celebrates Centenary

There was a very large turnout to celebrate the occasions.

In her welcome, the Chairman of the Friends, expressed thanks to all the staff over the years for giving of their best when it was needed most.

The Hospital Chaplain, Rev. Chris Brown, conducted a service of thanksgiving, and the Baptist Church Music Fellowship led the hymn singing. The Chairman of National Health Service Tayside paid tribute to the commitment and dedication of the doctors, nurses and all other staff, and the high clinical standards. He gave an assurance that everything was being done to support the link between local and specialist services.

A local MSP listed vision, inventiveness and determination as the qualities that had created the IMH.

The MSP and a resident shared the honour of cutting the cake. The secretary of the Friends, who organised the celebration, added the Friends' thanks to staff, present and past, and presented a copy of the celebration booklet to the senior GP, and also a framed portrait of the current staff.

The GP stressed how important it was that the rural Community Hospital had not been forgotten. He called for a sustained devotion to

Irvine Memorial Hospital Centenary Christmas card, 2002.

the highest standards of community healthcare. The MacNaughtons Vale of Atholl Pipe Band played as the gathering adjourned to the Hospital's beautiful therapeutical garden where in a happy atmosphere in fine weather, the MADCAPS concert party entertained on a Victorian theme.

The local MSP said "This is an appropriate opportunity to pay tribute to the community in Atholl who had the vision, the inventiveness and the determination to make this hospital a reality 100 years ago. Today as we debate the best facilities for the healthcare of our community, we need the same vision, inventiveness and determination in equal measure to our predecessors on the last century.

Today in Atholl, this community want a local healthcare facility that will draw together – ideally on one site – a new Community Hospital, a comprehensive Medical Centre and the dream of a single care home that will allow our elderly citizens to remain in the community they love and in which they are loved.

For some time I have been working with many others in the community to press Tayside Health Board, Perth & Kinross Council, Care Together and other public agencies to draw their plans together speedily to make this a reality.

Local facilities in the GP surgery and the hospital require to be modernised, and our community desperately requires a single care home that will meet the care needs of our elderly population and their families. Progress has been made, but the pace is terribly slow, and I hope today's event gives some new and fresh momentum to the discussions that are taking place.

Much good work has been done through this Hospital in the last 100 years, and I warmly compliment the doctors, nurses, auxiliary staff and other healthcare professionals who have served the community so well in this period. The Friends of the Hospital have also given enormously to develop this facility and I pay tribute to their efforts. There are strong foundations that we have to build on – and to meet the needs of current and future generations we must start that work now."

1978–2002

1978–2002 and Beyond – Irvine Memorial Hospital

1978 to 2002 seems to many a long time, but in reality, it is only a quarter of the time that the Irvine Memorial Hospital has stood as the centre, along with the general practices of this Locality of North West Perthshire, as one of the main providers of health care to this area.

Why 1978–2002? — that period is the time that I have been one of the Doctors in this community and have had the pleasure, the fun, the benefit, and the use of this hospital in helping deliver care to the patients of Pitlochry and beyond. A period of time during which I have had the pleasure of working alongside so many notable doctors, devoted nurses and committed health-care professionals.

To this day, I remain the only health-care professional and member of staff remaining that was in the employ of Tayside Health Board on August 1st 1978 – the date when I came from Dumfries to join Toberargan Surgery as a new young doctor – 'Boy David' by name – a name bestowed upon me by the then 'Matron' and her fellow nursing compatriots.

24 years has seen many changes – a name variation – Irvine Memorial Nursing Home to Irvine Memorial Hospital for one, – some progressive and very welcomed – other changes have had to be questioned, more so of late.

Who could believe, with the closure of Cuilindarach Home at Ballinluig in the early eighties, and the resulting separation of Health Care and Social Work Care, that some twenty plus years later, we should see Health Care and Social Work Care reunite again – under Care Together, to provide what is envisaged as seamless care to our patients and clients within our Communities. The buildings of the two twelve bed Continuing Care units at Aberfeldy and Pitlochry, along with the Social Work residential home at Dalweem, remain as evidence of that initial division of care. Today those care units are at the centre of emotive discussions regarding their future potential in serving the locality.

A comprehensive all-inclusive care of the elderly service along with all the expected medical services was developed over those years with excellent community support from all the Primary Health Care Team. Adequate sheltered housing along with residential care, acute hospital care and long-stay care with attached day hospital was available.

More recently a Day Centre at the Tryst completed the jigsaw of care. Irvine Memorial Hospital was the CENTRE of that care.

Now we see the dismantling of some of that service with no Continuing Care available and no Care of the Elderly Day Hospital at Irvine Memorial Hospital.

Acknowledgement is made of the arrival of the Dementia Unit and its Day Hospital but it is farewell to one service and welcome to another. Could not our patients still have benefited from both services, instead of having to be relocated outwith the community to which they belong, when that degree of care was required? Care provided over the years that I have been associated with this Community Hospital has always been of the highest of standards and acknowledged so by patient and relatives alike. It has progressed with new ideas and procedures being introduced timeously and appropriately with our Senior Nursing Colleagues, and more recently the Professions Associated with Medicine, leading the way in the delivery of this care – all to one end – to the benefit of our patients at whatever stage of their illness they may have reached.

Now we have to justify what we have to do – more so than ever and rightly so.

Protocols have to be written and implemented. Audit has to be seen to be carried out by all members of the Team – some to date are better than others at this. Appraisal of staff members has to be implemented annually. Even the GPs will have to be involved in this in the near future. Personal Revalidation for doctors is to be implemented by the General Medical Council in the near future. Clinical Governance is the in word – the monitoring of the quality of care that is delivered.

Many things that didn't exist in 1978 let alone 100 years ago.

What then for the future?

Can we provide the expected services and the quality of services from Irvine Memorial Hospital that Tayside Primary Care Trust, NHS Tayside and the Scottish Executive demand?

Can we deliver the standard of care that our patients and relatives expect?

Can we attract the staff to continue to deliver the caring, devoted and professional service that we, as providers of that service, would want to deliver to our patients?

The simple answer is Yes and No.

The provision of care is still of the highest standard, delivered by a team of dedicated and highly skilled professionals.

The staff can only provide that standard of care if the buildings and inherent resources are available and are modern, up-to-date, and built to an expected standard. This needs capital resources.

On-going Education to all our staff must be provided to continue to keep expected standards to the highest calibre.

In addition, local affordable housing has to be made available in the future to attract staff.

We give thanks for the hundred years that have been reached. This present generation has benefited from the foresight of those that came before.

We must now think what we can leave behind, for the benefit of the next generation within the Vale of Atholl.

The vision could be a new all-purpose Community Hospital linked to a Comprehensive Medical Centre – providing the services that a Community expects – built on a green-field site. Associated with this, in close proximity, a One Stop Care Home could be built so that our Senior Citizens can stay within the community with which they have long been associated.

That is the message I hear on a daily basis – a new Irvine Memorial Hospital for the future – a new Irvine Memorial Hospital to deliver care for the next 100 years.

When the next generation reads this, will that vision be a reality?

Let us be grateful for what has been provided for us – let us provide for the future.

Dr David Cruikshank,
General Practitioner, Toberargan Surgery, Pitlochry

2003

28th February 2003 – Huge Shake-up of Health and Care Proposed
Major proposals for the establishment of a community hospital, GP surgery, care home and social work office in Pitlochry have been approved in principle by councillors.

Members of the housing and adult care services committee gave Care Together the nod to enter into discussions over the plans, which centre on Bobbin Mill.

The development would radically redesign services within northwest Perthshire, would include:

- 11 GP beds
- 9 Dementia beds
- 26 Care Home beds
- 5 Dementia day places.

In a report put before councillors, the interim general manager of Care Together explained the key aims for the new service:

1) To address current environmental deficiencies through a new, single, fit-for-purpose building housing integrated health and social care provision for the catchment population.
2) To develop one-stop access to coordinated and seamless services.
3) To improve the equity and access to health and social care provision for the catchment population.

Given the ambitious and wide-ranging scope of the proposed development, it was admitted the changes would 'impact' on a huge range of existing services, including the IMH, Church of Scotland Chequers residential home, the Tryst day care centre and Toberargan GP surgery.

"The proposed development is being led by the Pitlochry GPs, NHS Tayside and the Church of Scotland."

It is anticipated that the development can be operational within two years.

"The care home provision included ... would be operated by the Church of Scotland and would offer the potential for a modern and integrated one-stop service for nursing and residential care.

This development will bring improvements in services within Pitlochry ... All of the current premises have outlived their life-spans.

This provides a unique opportunity to simultaneously develop a one-stop service."

The site at Bobbin Mill has been identified and a developer – Medical Centres Scotland Ltd – has been engaged.

Among anticipated outcomes would be the development of rehabilitation facilities in Aberfeldy to complement Pitlochry services, and improved access to services for people across north-west Perthshire.

As a further advantage, according to NHS Tayside, *"Local people would no longer have to leave the locality for care home provision because of a lack of choice".*

But he admits there are concerns.

The director of planning and development supports the development in principle, although he has concerns about whether the site is big enough to take all the proposed elements since no detailed plans have yet been produced.

The director of roads, transport and architectural services has concerns about whether the access to this site is suitable to serve a major development and about the impact of the additional traffic on the existing road network.

"When a planning application is received from the developers, the proposals will require to be advertised and will need to be referred to the Scottish Executive development department if the council has a financial interest in it."

Meanwhile, a council officer told elected members that the scheme would address a long-standing healthcare shortage. Local people would benefit by the service as they would not have to leave the area to receive care. Having to travel can cause a lot of hardship.

Care Together promised to report back to councillors on any progress.

2004

26th March 2004 – Town Looks to a Healthier Future

Healthcare in Highland Perthshire received a major boost this week with the announcement that a new healthcare facility will be created in Pitlochry.

All the existing services at the local IMH, Toberargan GP surgery and the residential care provided by the Chequers Church of Scotland home will be combined.

And the new facilities will provide nursing care for the elderly.

The News was warmly welcomed by the local MSP who attended a packed public meeting – organised by Pitlochry Community Council and Friends of IMH – at Pitlochry Town Hall on Wednesday evening.

The MSP said

"I am absolutely delighted with the plans to develop a new state-of-the-art community healthcare facility in Pitlochry fit for the 21st century.

Not only will there be the continuation of existing healthcare services but in a new setting, there will be new facilities added such as the long-term nursing care service and the opportunity for the use of telemedicine services.

The new facilities mean that elderly and frail people in Highland Perthshire will be able to remain in the community and their nursing care rather than be moved out of the area to Crieff, Blairgowrie, Perth or further afield.

A telemedicine service also means that local residents will be able to receive test results and other advice locally rather than have to travel to Perth and Dundee for these services."

The MSP added, *"The plans are still in outline, but they are an exciting and visionary development. I pay tribute to NHS Tayside, Perth & Kinross Council, the Church of Scotland, the GP practice and the developers who have worked closely together for many years to reach this point.*

I have taken a keen and long-standing interest in this project. Too many of my elderly constituents have had to leave the area for care due to the absence of nursing care in the locality. Many constituents have also had to make frequent journeys to other hospitals for advice, and I am optimistic some of the services can be provided locally.

In trying to advance agreement for this development, I have had regular discussions with the chairman of NHS Tayside and enlisted the support of the Health Minister.

Both of these have seen this project as an innovative new development in rural healthcare provision and the personal .... and this project has been much appreciated by me and the local community.

The involvement of the local community – particularly the Friends of Chequers and the IMH – has helped to maintain pressure for this development."

2005

30th April 2005 – New Health and Social Care Centre for Pitlochry

The planned development of a new health and social care centre for Pitlochry appears to have been pulled back from the brink of total collapse.

But its survival depends on more meetings between top-level officials who have yet to agree the way forward.

Senior officials from NHS Tayside, Perth & Kinross Council's social work services, and the Church of Scotland, along with local GP representatives all met in Perth Royal Infirmary yesterday to try and ensure 'a positive outcome'.

Thus, followed fears that major parts of the project were in jeopardy and threatening what was meant to be a single development taken forward by a number of partners working together for the benefit of patients.

It is understood Scotland's Minister for Health took a close interest after a local paper published concerns about the future of the project intended for the town's community hospital, overcrowded GP surgery and other community services on one site at the Bobbin Mill.

A local GP, the senior partner at Toberargan Surgery, went on record with his concerns after 'final plans' that had been put on public display in the local library had to be changed after a last-minute withdrawal by social work. They had originally agreed to locate offices on the top floor of the development.

More crucially for the people of Pitlochry and its surrounding area was the perceived threat to the nursing care bed provision on the site due to a wrangle between the Church of Scotland and the Council over appropriate funding of these beds.

There are no nursing homes in north-west Perthshire and provision of nursing beds was seen as a key part of the development.

Clearly there was full and frank discussion at yesterday's meeting but the different parties were wary of saying anything at all afterwards beyond advising that a joint statement would be issued. Even the previously vocal GP declined to comment, not wishing to jeopardise what appeared to be progress yesterday.

While the Bobbin Mill project has been six years in development and should have been up and running by now, nobody was yet giving it the green light yesterday, but it seems enough has now been done to focus the minds of senior managers in all partner organisations to find a resolution and get the builders on site as soon as possible.

The project partners issued the following statement after the meeting:

"We have had a very positive meeting and made good progress. We now have a set of proposals which we hope will prove acceptable to all partners.

The details of the proposals will be considered by the various governing bodies involved over the next few weeks and we are hopeful that all the bodies will be able to sign off the proposals on the table.

The key partners have committed to taking these proposals forward and, subject to agreement, we are confident that this will bring the programme for development back on track. It remains the intention to deliver modern purpose-built facilities for the community of Pitlochry and surrounding area to improve the provision of locally-based care by early 2007.

Although it has taken us longer than we would have liked to get to this stage, this is a visionary scheme which demonstrates excellent partnership working for the people of the community in N.W. Perthshire."

The local MSP, who has backed the development from its inception, said last night, *"I am very pleased to hear of the progress that has been made at the discussions today and hope this signals the final phase in the planning of this important new healthcare facility. I encourage all the parties involved to work swiftly to secure final agreement to enable early development of the site. This development has been a long time in the planning and I hope today's news signals the clearing of the final hurdle in what has been a long race for the people of Pitlochry."*

May 2005 – Deputy Minister Backs Plans
The Deputy Health Minister yesterday placed on record support for the Bobbin Mill project.

The local MSP raised the subject at yesterday's First Minister's Question Time in the Scottish Parliament.

The MSP has expressed disappointment at the withdrawal earlier this week of the Church of Scotland from the project to provide a replacement for the community hospital and local GPs' surgery along with integrated nursing care provision.

The Church had been involved in planning the project for four years with the intention of providing the nursing care element.

Yesterday the local MSP told the Deputy Health Minister it was *"regrettable"* the Church had pulled out at *"a very late stage"* and asked the Minister to assure his constituents that a new community hospital and GP surgery would go ahead.

The Minister said she was aware of the Pitlochry project and said she was *"encouraged"* that NHS Tayside had made it quite clear there would be a new community hospital and replacement GP surgery. Steps were being taken to find an alternative provider for the nursing care element.

17th May 2005 – Pulling Out

Plans for a purpose-built integrated health and social care centre for Pitlochry are in jeopardy after a last minute withdrawal by the Church of Scotland.

The Church of Scotland is withdrawing from the integrated health and social care project at Bobbin Mill, Pitlochry. It seems the Kirk was influenced by the scale of running costs. The social work department has also reneged, pleading changed priorities.

What is left is the community hospital and GP surgery. The grand plan has been drastically revised, as grand plans often are, but at least the medical core is to be retained.

The Kirk had planned to provide 26 nursing care beds for patients in need of continuing care as part of the development on the bobbin Mill site, but yesterday confirmed they were withdrawing from the project.

After being closely involved in the development for four years, the Kirk decided it simply could not afford to proceed. It is understood the Kirk had no problem committing the capital required for its share of the development, but at the last minute, baulked at the running costs. The Kirk's lead negotiator, who only 10 days ago put his name to a positive statement on the future of the joint development, refused to answer questions.

The Council's Director of Social said he was *"not entering into any discussion"*. He issued the following statement:

> *"The Church of Scotland's Board of Social Responsibility has, with regret, has had to announce its withdrawal from the proposed integrated health and social care development at Bobbin Mill in Pitlochry.*
>
> *It is particularly disappointing after many years of planning in the hope that the Church could be part of this exciting development. Unfortunately, the costs of the Church's involvement in this project have become too great, and the board would not be able to sustain the significant loss that would accrue if it continued with this project.*
>
> *The Board of Social Responsibility deeply regrets this decision, but remains committed to the continued operation of Chequers Residential Home in Pitlochry until there is a replacement home equipped and prepared for the future to meet the needs of vulnerable older people in Pitlochry and north west Perthshire."*

The Kirk's decision to pull out came as a hammer blow to other partners in the development who nevertheless said they would proceed with the plans and look for an alternative to the Church of Scotland.

The senior partner GP at Toberargan Surgery, due for replacement as part of the development, said he was *"mystified"* how what had been a *"very positive"* meeting between representatives of various bodies involved in the development on 29th April became *"an extremely negative presentation to the Kirk's Board of Social Responsibility a few days later."*

The senior GP said that at the meeting of April 29, the Director of social Work was *"extremely positive"* that he would be able to convince his executive the Bobbin Mill was a *"going concern."*

The GP agreed there was still *"a funding gap"* but said the project partners were *"confident it could be met"*. He said the new surgery and community hospital would go ahead, with a planned opening in early 2007.

"It's just not the integrated health and social care project we had hoped for", he said, adding there was still no nursing care provision in north west Perthshire which the planned Church of Scotland element of the project

was intended to address.

Chequers is a residential home in Pitlochry that requires a different level of staffing and has a less dependent population than a nursing care development.

The General Manager of Perth & Kinross Community Health Partnership, who has represented NHS Tayside in the negotiations on the Bobbin Mill project, responded to the news of the Kirk's withdrawal:

> *"We are extremely disappointed that the Church of Scotland has pulled out of this development at this very late stage, having been involved in the planning for over four years. They have confirmed that they are withdrawing from the project and this came as a complete surprise to us.*
>
> *We can, however, give an assurance that the new community hospital and new GP surgery will go ahead as planned later this year.*
>
> *We will now be exploring what options are open to us for the provision of care home places".*

Following the disappointment of the Church of Scotland and the Social Work Department stepping down from the integrated health and social care project at Bobbin Mill, Pitlochry, a local paper reported various opinions by local and political persons; these comments reflected the disappointment and the lack of care by government for rural areas for the elderly and general health care.

Later in May 2005 – NHS Chief Attacked Over Care Project

An MSP has branded the NHS Tayside Chairman ignorant and/or foolish after he waded into the row over the future of the Bobbin Mill scheme in Pitlochry.

Following the withdrawal of the Church of Scotland from the health and social care development, the NHS Tayside Chairman said he was *"utterly disappointed"* and heavily criticised the Church for *"walking away"* from the project.

A local MSP insisted no blame should be attached to the Church and turned his ire on the NHS chief, telling him to spend less time *"playing political games"* and more time improving care provision.

"The financial pressures on care home providers are well known," the MSP said.

"The Scottish Executive needs to address the long-term under-funding of care places which has created a crisis in the sector across the country."

The NHS Chair said the Executive was not to blame for the current situation and any suggestion otherwise was *"totally unacceptable and completely wrong"*.

The MSP responded. *"I am surprised that a public servant such as the Chairman feels it is part of his role to enter the party political field and seek to defend his political masters in the Scottish Executive.*

I am not sure this is appropriate conduct for someone who is paid to help deliver health care to Tayside residents.

Anyone with an iota of knowledge about health issues knows there is a serious issue about funding of care home places by the Executive – an issue which I and my Conservative colleagues have raised in the Scottish Parliament on numerous occasions, as recently as last week."

The MSP did not hold back in his criticism of the NHS Tayside chairman:

> *"Either the Chairman is ignorant of these issues, which I find hard to believe, or he is foolishly straying into the political field in defence of the policies of the Labour/Liberal Democrat Scottish Executive,"* he said. *"He would be well advised to spend less time playing political games and more time trying to help increase care home provision for local residents.*
>
> *The Church of Scotland has pulled out of the Bobbin Mill project for financial reasons, and I have a great deal of sympathy for them.*
>
> *I sincerely hope that another private sector provider can be found, but we all know the financial pressures they are under, and this fundamental issue has to be addressed."*

3rd June 2005 – Public Meeting

A newspaper report appeared encouraging the public to attend the meeting on 28th June 2005 when it was hoped all would be made clearer and the hope of putting together a hospital, GP surgery and a nursing care home would be in close proximity to each other, would be explained.

27th June 2005 – Public Meeting
Once again, a local paper offered an article encouraging the people of Highland Perthshire to attend the meeting on 28th June about the development of the Bobbin Mill site. It was started that as well as explaining the current position on the project, the meeting will include an opportunity for the public to ask questions of the NHS people involved. There was side-stepping, and indirect replies, ending with little or no further information, only an impression that it would happen regardless of local opinion.

28th June 2005 – A Public Information Event
Little information was forthcoming from the meeting.

30th November 2005 – Ambitious Plans of New Health Body
An innovative new health body launched yesterday in Perth has revealed ambitious plans to renovate a building labelled as an 'eyesore' and build new health centres in Kinross and Pitlochry.

The article speaks at length about Cornhill House, but in a later paragraph:

The CHP also announced plans to build a seven-bed in-patient unit for dementia sufferers at Bobbin Mill, Pitlochry.

It will also have nine GP beds, a casualty/minor injury unit, outpatient facilities, therapy areas and a GP surgery.

The aim is to include an ambulance base at the unit, manned by personnel from the Scottish Ambulance Service.

Work should begin on the site in February/March and be completed by June/July 2007.

2006

11th February 2006 – Work on Pitlochry Hospital set to Start
The creation of a new Pitlochry hospital, GP surgery and care home at Bobbin Mill is now scheduled to go ahead in the spring.

Work on the Pitlochry Integrated Care Development, which will deliver modern, purpose-built medical care facilities, will start shortly with a planned completion date of next autumn. The project has been nearly seven years in the planning and on a number of occasions has seemed doomed to failure.

However, planning permission has been obtained for the medical facilities and it is hoped permission will be granted for the care home before summer.

NHS Tayside is working in partnership with Toberargan practice, Perth & Kinross Council and Medical Centres Scotland to help deliver a first-class facility for the people of Pitlochry and north-west Perthshire.

More than 200 people packed into Pitlochry Town Hall last month to hear revised plans for health and social care in the area.

The first phase will see the creation of a replacement community hospital and new GP surgery/health centre on the Bobbin Mill site, with funding already in place.

The second phase will see the development of a new stand-alone care home at the same site.

Negotiations are under way between the developers and a number of care home providers to identify a partner to own and operate a care home.

In addition, negotiations have been advanced with the Scottish Ambulance Service to relocate the ambulance base to Bobbin Mill.

Plans are already under way for the new therapeutic garden, hospital radio in conjunction with Heartland Radio, and several other projects which the Friends hope to fund.

A spokesman for the developers Medical Centres Scotland added *"Provided planning consent is granted and the commercial and legal documentation completed by Easter, construction of the care home will begin in the summer. The whole development is programmed to finish at the same time in autumn 2007".*

2008

20th August 2008 – New Hospital Hailed as fit for 21st Century
A new multi-million-pound community hospital in Pitlochry was yesterday hailed as meeting *"patient needs in the 21st century".*

Cabinet Secretary Nicola Sturgeon officially opened the doors of Pitlochry Community Hospital, which includes a GP surgery, seven bed dementia assessment unit and a care home.

The opening of Pitlochry's Community Hospital by Nicola Sturgeon.

The £7.09 million building at Bobbin Mill also has a minor injuries unit, outpatient clinic, social work department, casualty service and facility for occupational therapy and speech and language development. It houses all services and patients transferred for Irvine Memorial Hospital.

Ms Sturgeon praised the building and said she believed community hospitals have a crucial role for the NHS.

> *"This hospital represents a new generation of community facilities designed to meet patients' needs in the 21st century.*
>
> *Shifting the balance of care from the main acute hospital centres to local communities wherever it's clinically safe and sensible to do so is a key goal for the NHS in Scotland. Community hospitals have a crucial role to play here.*
>
> *I don't think we can over-emphasise how important it is to people to have access to local services and to avoid the need to travel to larger centres. It's therefore great to see a wide range of out-patient clinics and other services being delivered from a hospital in the heart of the community."*

A local MSP said, *"I think this is the type of 21st century project that rural communities require, and it is great to see that in Pitlochry and Highland Perthshire".*

Another local MSP said, *"The new hospital is an excellent facility that has a superb and caring workforce. The local GPs, nurses and staff provide care for the local residents to such a high degree and it is only fitting that they have a hospital that reflects their great work for the community".*

The Chairman of NHS Tayside said that the Hospital reinforced NHS Tayside's commitment to bring first-class health services to the heart of local communities and reflected the hard work and dedication of staff.

"The NHS in Scotland has been celebrating its 60th anniversary, so it seems fitting NHS Tayside is able to mark the anniversary with the opening of the state-of-the-art facility."

The partners in the scheme were the Atholl Medical Practice, NHS Tayside, Perth & Kinross Community Health Partnership, the Scottish Ambulance Service, Balhousie Care Homes and Medical Centres Scotland (MCS).

A Service of Blessing and Dedication of the New Pitlochry Community Hospital and Atholl Unit
SATURDAY, 8TH MARCH 2008
CALL TO WORSHIP

PSALM 127
Unless the Lord builds the house,
its builders labour in vain.
Unless the Lord watches over the city,
the watchmen stand guard in vain.

HYMN
'Guide me O thou Great Redeemer'
Guide me, O Thou great Redeemer
Pilgrim through this barren land.

I am weak, but Thou art mighty;
Hold me with Thy powerful hand.
Bread of Heaven, Bread of Heaven,
Feed me till I want no more;
Feed me till I want no more.

Open now the crystal fountain,
Whence the healing stream doth flow;
Let the fire and cloudy pillar
Lead me all my journey through.
Strong Deliverer, strong Deliverer,
Be Thou still my Strength and Shield;
Be Thou still my Strength and Shield.

When I tread the verge of Jordan,
Bid my anxious fears subside;
Death of deaths, and hell's destruction,
Land me safe on Canaan's side.
Songs of praises, songs of praises,
I will ever give to Thee;
I will ever give to Thee.

PSALM 100

Shout for joy to the Lord all the earth.
Worship the Lord with gladness; come before him
with joyful songs.
Know that the Lord is God. It is he who made us, and
we are his; we are his people, the sheep of his pasture.
Enter his gates with thanksgiving and his courts
with praise; give thanks to him and praise his name.
For the Lord is good and his love endures forever;
his faithfulness continues through all generations.

MATTHEW 25:31-40

When the Son of Man comes in his glory, and all the angels with him,
then he will sit on the throne of his glory. All the nations will be gathered

before him, and he will separate people one from another as a shepherd separates the sheep from the goats, and he will put the sheep at his right hand and the goats at the left. Then the king will say to those at his right hand, *"Come, you that are blessed by my Father, inherit the kingdom prepared for you from the foundation of the world; for I was hungry and you gave me food, I was thirsty and you gave me something to drink, I was a stranger and you welcomed me, I was naked and you gave me clothing, I was sick and you took care of me, I was in prison and you visited me"*. Then the righteous will answer him, *"Lord, when was it that we saw you hungry and gave you food, or thirsty and gave you something to drink? And when was it that we saw you a stranger and welcomed you, or naked and gave you clothing? And when was it that we saw you sick or in prison and visited you?"* And the king will answer them, *"Truly I tell you, just as you did it to one of the least of these who are members of my family"*.

ADDRESS

An old woman by the name of Miss McBain lived in a wee croft in the Cabrach, in Morayshire all her life. In the mid 1970s the laird of the Glenfiddich Estate told her that they were going to put electricity into her house. But she'd managed 80 years without electricity and wasn't too fussy about having it now.

Six months later Miss Mc Bain's croft was fully electrified. The laird dropped in past to see her one day expecting to hear how life had been made so much easier with the electric lights, cooker, fridge, heating and so on... *"Oh I'm much happier now"* said Miss McBain. *"Now that I've got the electric light, I've got peace of mind if ever I run out of paraffin for my lamps or peats for the fire!"* And as far as I know, her paraffin never did run out and neither did her supply of peats, and so the electricity was never required. Miss McBain had great peace of mind, but never did adapt to the new ways of working.

This wee service is all about expressing our thanks for this wonderful new hospital, which I'm pleased to say, is fully electrified. But it's so much more than simply giving thanks for a new building; It's about giving thanks for new ways of working. For the first time, we have the GP surgery, the hospital, the social work department, the ambulance depot, and later in the year, care for the elderly, quite literally under the one roof.

And that must give us great peace of mind, as well as potentially the greatest health care we've ever known in Highland Perthshire. Adapting to these new ways will surely be a blessing and an advantage in itself.

But we ask for a greater blessing upon all this and all that the future holds in this new hospital. We ask for God's blessing on this wonderful resource of buildings, equipment, and the people who will work here and contribute to our health care. God's blessing on the new ways which promise an even higher standard of care and attention for all ages and generations yet to come.

Amen.

PRAYER OF DEDICATION

Almighty God, whose Son Jesus Christ taught us that what we do for the least of our brothers and sisters we do also for him; we pray your blessing upon this new building, the technology, the equipment and the resources, and all who serve to care for our health, body mind and soul.

We give you thanks for new ways of working together and the many possibilities that the future holds. For the advances that have been made in health care and medical research. We give you thanks for those who will contribute to the healing process, who will encourage, support, comfort, and guide. And we welcome your presence to remain here in the life of this hospital in the community for which it serves.

Bless this place to the glory of your name and to the benefit of your children.

Through Jesus Christ our Lord, hear our prayer.

Amen.

HYMN
'Will you Come and Follow Me'
Tune: 'Kelvingrove'

Will you come and follow me if I but call your name?
Will you go where you don't know and never be the same?
Will you let my love be shown? Will you let my name be known,
will you let my life be grown in you and you in me?
Will you leave yourself behind if I but call your name?
Will you care for cruel and kind and never be the same?
Will you risk the hostile stare should your life attract or scare?

Will you let me answer prayer in you and you in me?

Will you let the blinded see if I but call your name?
Will you set the prisoners free and never be the same?
Will you kiss the leper clean and do such as this unseen,
and admit to what I mean in you and you in me?

Will you love the "you" you hide if I but call your name?
Will you quell the fear inside and never be the same?
Will you use the faith you've found to reshape the world around,
through my sight and touch and sound in you and you in me?

Lord your summons echoes true when you but call my name.
Let me turn and follow you and never be the same.
In Your company I'll go where Your love and footsteps show.
Thus I'll move and live and grow in you and you in me.

BLESSING
The peace and blessing of almighty God,
Rest upon this place,
Upon all who enter it and go out from it,
And upon all who dwell under this roof.
In the name of the Father, and of the Son,
And of the Holy Ghost.
Amen.

A Service of Celebration and Remembrance for the Irvine Memorial Hospital, Pitlochry
Pitlochry – Church of Scotland
14 July 1902 – 14 March 2008
Sunday, 2nd March 2008, 4.00 pm

WELCOME
The Reverend Ian Murray, Hospital Chaplain.
Tea and Coffee in Tryst
Next Saturday, 11am Open day beginning with Service of dedication.

CALL TO WORSHIP
Romans 13
Owe no-one anything, except to love one another,
for he who loves his neighbour has fulfilled the law.

HYMN
Psalm 100
'All People that on Earth do Dwell'
All people that on earth do dwell,
Sing to the Lord with cheerful voice.
Him serve with fear, His praise forth tell;
Come ye before Him and rejoice.

The Lord, ye know, is God indeed;
Without our aid He did us make;
We are His folk, He doth us feed,
And for His sheep He doth us take.

O enter then His gates with praise;
Approach with joy His courts unto;
Praise, laud, and bless His Name always,
For it is seemly so to do.

For why? the Lord our God is good;
His mercy is for ever sure;

His truth at all times firmly stood,
And shall from age to age endure.

To Father, Son and Holy Ghost,
The God Whom Heaven and earth adore,
From men and from the angel host
Be praise and glory evermore.

PRAYER
The Reverend Malcolm Ramsay

Holy God, help us to be so sure of the eternal that we can be at peace in the movement of time, and let us so see you in the things of time that we may know ourselves to be part of the eternal. As you have loved and cherished us so may we love and cherish one another, and in learning to love ourselves come to love you in all life.

Lord Jesus Christ, our great Physician and Friend, draw near to us in our remembrance and thanksgiving for the life of our hospital. That in remembering the past and celebrating those who have gone before us, we might be better equipped to look to the future and continue their good works of care and support.

Almighty God, whose Son Jesus Christ has taught us that what we do for the least of our brothers and sisters, we do also for him; grant us the will to be the servant of others as he was the servant of all. Through Jesus Christ our saviour. Amen.

READINGS

LUKE 10:25-37
Read by Jim McGuinness, Hospital Administrator

On one occasion an expert in the law stood up to test Jesus. *"Teacher"*, he asked, *"what must I do to inherit eternal life?"*

"What is written in the Law?" he replied. *"How do you read it?"*

He answered: " *'Love the Lord your God with all your heart and with all your soul and with all your strength and with all your mind'; and, 'Love your neighbour as yourself'"*.

"You have answered correctly", Jesus replied. *"Do this and you will live."*

146

But he wanted to justify himself, so he asked Jesus, *"And who is my neighbour?"*

In reply Jesus said: *"A man was going down from Jerusalem to Jericho, when he fell into the hands of robbers. They stripped him of his clothes, beat him and went away, leaving him half dead. A priest happened to be going down the same road, and when he saw the man, he passed by on the other side. So too, a Levite, when he came to the place and saw him, passed by on the other side. But a Samaritan, as he travelled, came where the man was; and when he saw him, he took pity on him. He went to him and bandaged his wounds, pouring on oil and wine. Then he put the man on his own donkey, took him to an inn and took care of him. The next day he took out two silver coins and gave them to the innkeeper. 'Look after him', he said, 'and when I return, I will reimburse you for any extra expense you may have'.*

Which of these three do you think was a neighbour to the man who fell into the hands of robbers?"

The expert in the law replied, *"The one who had mercy on him".*

Jesus told him, *"Go and do likewise".*

MARK 10:46-52
Read by Christine Schmitt Mackinnon

As Jesus was leaving Jericho with his disciples and a great multitude, Bartimaeus, a blind beggar, was sitting by the roadside. And when he heard that it was Jesus of Nazareth, he began to cry out and say, *"Jesus, Son of David, have mercy on me!"* And many rebuked him, telling him to be silent; but he cried out all the more, *"Son of David, have mercy on me!"* And Jesus stopped and said, *"Call him".* And they called the blind man; saying to him, *"Take heart; rise, he is calling you".* And throwing off his mantle he sprang up and came to Jesus. And Jesus said to him, *"What do you want me to do for you?"* And the blind man said to him, *"Master, let me receive my sight".* And Jesus said to him, *"Go your way; your faith has made you well".* And immediately he received his sight and followed him on the way.

HYMN
'We Cannot Measure How You Heal'
We cannot measure how you heal,
or answer every sufferer's prayer,

Yet we believe your grace responds
where faith and love unite to care.
Your hands, though bloodied on the cross,
survive to hold and heal and warn,
To carry all through death to life
and cradle children yet unborn.

The pain that will not go away,
the guilt that clings from things long past,
The fear of what the future holds,
are present as if meant to last.
But present too is love which tends
the hurt we never hoped to find,
The private agonies inside,
the memories that haunt the mind.

So some have come who need your help
and some have come to make amends
As hands which shaped and saved the world
are present in the touch of friends.
Lord, let your Spirit meet us here
to mend the body, mind, and soul.
To disentangle peace from pain
and make your broken people whole.

REFLECTION

A couple of weeks ago an old friend in Aberdeenshire celebrated his 100th birthday. He had a wonderful party with many people travelling great distances to share in the celebrations. One of the most special presents he received was a book of photographs and stories collected from family and friends spanning the whole of his life. Together, these memories painted a fuller picture of the man, giving a strong sense of his character. Most of us certain parts of his life, but none of us really knew the whole story.

It struck me just how much we use our memories to make our identity; as individuals, as a family, and as communities. We make our memories and in many ways our memories make us.

Today is very much about thanksgiving for many different memories – personal and shared memories of the Irvine Memorial Hospital. Each one of us gathered here today has our own thoughts and experiences of the hospital, whether as staff, present or retired, or as a next of kin to a loved one who lived out their last days in the care of the hospital, or perhaps as a patient, we all have our memories and experiences for which we are thankful. I would guess, that one way or another, every family living in these communities, has depended upon the care of the Irvine Memorial Hospital at one time or another.

Looking right back at the beginning, the story of how the Irvine Memorial Nursing Home came into being, is a fascinating one.

It was on the 14th of July 1902 that the official opening took place, named after the late Dr William Stewart Irvine, who had faithfully served the local community for almost 60 years.

Prior to the opening of the hospital, the only nurses in the area were those privately employed by wealthy families. These private nurses helped attend the needs of the employees of the estates and were occasionally permitted to tend to the needs of others in the community. And there were also one or two local women who were paid by the parish to tend people who were too poor to pay for necessary help. This assistance was in the beginning, untrained but as a result of money subscribed nationally by Queen Victoria's Silver Jubilee, a formalised system of training district nurses was established.

In 1894 one of Pitlochry's doctors, Dr Beatty, proposed that funds should be raised to employ a *Queen's Nurse*. The Pitlochry District Nursing Association was almost immediately set up under the supervision of Miss Molyneux of Tom-na-Monachan House (now the Pine Trees Hotel). And the first fully trained nurse began in Pitlochry in December 1895 at a salary of £60 per annum.

By the summer of 1896 plans were afoot to keep alive in some beneficial way, the memory of Dr William Stewart Irvine. And over the following six months almost £500 was raised from the local community, mainly through the efforts of Miss Henrietta McInroy of Lude Estate in Blair Atholl. In the spring of 1887, Miss McInroy of Lude proposed that the monies raised should be handed over to the Pitlochry District Nursing Association to establish a nursing home, but the committee, still under the chairmanship of Miss Molyneux turned down the offer suggesting that Miss McInroy use the funds for the building of a Home for Old People. Miss McInroy persisted but still, unanimously the committee agreed that a Cottage Hospital was not required. Eventually the funds were accepted for the purpose of building a home for the district nurse with a room for the reception of one or two patients. Sadly, Miss McInroy never saw her dream as she died only a few weeks later. Her memorial plaque is on the back wall of Blair Atholl Parish Church.

With Miss McInroy's money in place and further local fundraising and several beneficiaries, a sight was offered by Mr Fergusson of Baledmund, opposite the Old Baptist Manse, now *Mansewood on Nursing Home Brae.* But despite the committee's assurances that the Home was not for *'Infectious Cases, nor for Epilepsy or Mental Diseases'*, the sight had to be abandoned due to the opposition from the neighbours. In December 1901, after a considerable search for a new sight, the present site to the north of the Old Baptist Manse was settled upon and the building commenced.

The Irvine Nursing Home was publically opened on the 14th of July 1902 by the Reverend Duncan Campbell of St. Matthew's Church Edinburgh – an old friend of Dr Irvine. The cost of the build, Male and female wards with separate bathrooms, nurses' rooms, a kitchen and an office with well laid out grounds, came to £1,376.5s.6d. (about £100,000 in today's money) Those early years, in fact right up until the formation of the NHS in 1948, were dependent upon local benefactors and fundraising from within the community.

And I could go on and on ... with extensions to the building in 1907, 1929, 1936 and the Atholl Ward in 1980. and so much more ... but for the moment, that touches on the early history of the Irvine Memorial Nursing Home.

HYMN
(Paraphrase 2)
'O God of Bethel!'

O God of Bethel, by Whose hand
Thy people still are fed,
Who through this weary pilgrimage
Hast all our fathers led.

Our vows, our prayers, we now present
Before Thy throne of grace;
God of our fathers, be the God
Of their succeeding race.

Through each perplexing path of life
Our wandering footsteps guide;
Give us each day our daily bread,
And raiment fit provide.

O spread Thy covering wings around
Till all our wanderings cease,
And at our Father's loved abode
Our souls arrive in peace.

Such blessings from Thy gracious hand
Our humble prayers implore;
And Thou shalt be our chosen God,
And portion evermore.

My old friend in Aberdeenshire was delighted with the book of photographs and stories he was presented on his 100th birthday, but it was clearly the photographs and stories about the people rather than the places that brought most delight.

The life of the Irvine Memorial Hospital is that which brings together the contributions from countless nurses, doctors, and all the other staff, therapists, cleaners, cooks, and so on all manifest in the love and care of patients and their wider families.

I'm going to ask retired Matron, Ruby Ripley to share some of her memories of her thirteen years at the Irvine Memorial Hospital.

A MATRON REMEMBERS
Ruby Ripley
Reflection

From the New Testament we heard the story of blind Bartimaeus. A man desperate to be healed.

And Jesus response was to take this man, Bartimaeus, seriously and make him the centre of attention. The patient centred approach is not new. What is interesting is Jesus' question to Bartimaeus. *"What do you want me to do for you?"* And if the answer is obvious, but why does Jesus ask the question?

Perhaps Jesus wants Bartimaeus to think carefully, to take an active part in his own healing, not just leave it to Jesus. As if healing involves the whole person, body mind and soul.

And so to the present day. It is to this holistic care we are committed to in the NHS.

Our staff are overwhelmingly dedicated to providing the highest of standards, with great professionalism and dedication, often working under enormous pressure.

Jesus's question, *"What do you want me to do for you?"* could well be on the lips of doctors, nurses, chaplains, or anyone in the NHS today.

And I'm sure it's been the question asked many times before in the life of the Irvine Memorial Hospital.

But when we ask that question today, we must be sure that we can follow up the response with the highest provision of care. And that can only be done if the buildings and resources are available and up-to date.

Someone asked me during the week, *"what time is the funeral service for the Irvine Memorial on Sunday?"* And I must say, it does feel a little like a funeral service. Because with all good funeral services, all good celebrations of life, there is ultimately hope and reassurance of new life – a new beginning.

What we have had in the past, we remember and are truly thankful for.

For those with great enthusiasm and determination who first established the Hospital, and those who have played a part in its expansion and progress over the 106 years.

For the many countless people who have benefited in one way or another from the love and care of the Irvine Memorial Hospital. For the many staff who have dedicated their lives to the physical, mental, and spiritual care of patients and families in our communities.

And of course, for the work and efforts of many volunteers, the League of Friends which has been on the go since 1974. The Family Support Group for the Atholl Ward started by Veronica Charity in 1991, not to mention the visits, usually around Christmas time from the school children and the brownies.

And we give thanks for all of this, in the knowledge that our future promises an even higher standard of health care for all ages, for many generations yet to come.

Amen.

CHOIR
'Gloria, gloria, in excelsis Deo!'

PRAYERS
Prayers led by
Nurse Jean Spinner
Mr Jim McGuinness
Dr David Cruikshank
Revd Ian Murray

God our Creator, we give you thanks today for the wonderful opportunity of life, with all its joys and responsibilities, its experiences and opportunities, its risks, and uncertainties. We give you thanks for role of the Irvine Memorial Hospital in our community and the many people who have played a part in its life.

And so, we pray, each from our own experiences.

As a Nurse I pray for all who have tended the sick. For all who have contributed to the healing process and given comfort in the darkest hours of distress and fear.

For today's nurses and for those yet to come, give to our eyes light to see those in need. Give to our hearts compassion and understanding.

Give to our minds, knowledge, and wisdom. Give to our hands, skill, and tenderness, and to our ears, the ability to listen.

As a Hospital Administrator I pray with thanksgiving for those who have contributed to the organisation and management of the Irvine Memorial Hospital.

For those, who at the beginning, worked with determination and foresight to help create the hospital we know today. For today's administrators, grant us the strength to ensure our hospitals operate efficiently and provide adequate medical care to patients. Help us to fulfil our responsibilities in assisting the medical and support staff; to organise, direct, control and coordinate medical and health services. As the medical staff strive to keep the blood flowing and the heart beating, bless the hospital administrator in keeping the hospital alive and healthy.

As a Doctor I pray with thanksgiving for the devotion and wisdom of Dr William Stewart Irvine, and every other Doctor who has served in this community.

With humility, help us to increase our skills and respect those who teach and broaden our knowledge. In turn, enable us to freely impart our knowledge and wisdom to others. Enable us to fulfil our medical calling in love, wisdom, and integrity. Give us knowledge and diligence in the prevention, diagnosis, and treatment of disease. Help us to bring comfort to the anxious and fearful.

Strengthen us to persevere in the face of fatigue, and with God's blessing, respect the sanctity of human life.

As a Chaplain I pray with thanksgiving for all those who have sought to provide spiritual care, comfort, and support within the Irvine Memorial Hospital.

Receive our thanksgiving for those who comfort other's lives when they are emotionally wounded and struggling. Grant that all who bring spiritual care may be sensitive in their ministry, understanding in sharing others burdens, and supportive in times of sorrow.

Help us to rejoice with those who rejoice, and weep with those who weep, and so continue the service of Christ, who taught us to say:

Our Father, who art in heaven,
hallowed be thy name;
thy kingdom come;
thy will be done,
on earth as it is in heaven.
Give us this day our daily bread.
And forgive us our debts,
as we forgive those who debt against us.
And lead us not into temptation;
as we forgive those who debt against us.
And lead us not into temptation;
but deliver us from evil.
For thine is the kingdom,
the power and the glory,
for ever and ever.
Amen.

HYMN

'Tell out my Soul, the Greatness of the Lord'
(Woodlands)

Tell out, my soul, the greatness of the Lord!
Unnumbered blessings give my spirit voice;
tender to me the promise of his word;
in God my Saviour shall my heart rejoice.
Tell out, my soul, the greatness of his Name!
Make known his might, the deeds his arm has done;
his mercy sure, from age to age to same;
his holy Name – the Lord, the Mighty One.
Tell out, my soul, the greatness of his might!
Powers and dominions lay their glory by.
Proud hearts and stubborn wills are put to flight,
the hungry fed, the humble lifted high.
Tell out, my soul, the glories of his word!
Firm is his promise, and his mercy sure.
Tell out, my soul, the greatness of the Lord
to children's children and for evermore!

BLESSING

May the eternal Creator give you courage to carry the past gently in your souls. May the eternal Son give you strength to live each day in his presence. May the eternal Spirit give you wisdom to face the future without fear.

And the blessing of God almighty: the Father, the Son and the Holy Spirit be with you and remain with you this day and for ever.

Amen.

2009

Former Hospital to be Sold Off

A disused Pitlochry hospital is to be sold off, if a buyer can be found in the current economic climate, writes a health reporter.

Irvine Memorial Hospital has been vacant since 'services transferred to the new purpose-built community hospital on the Bobbin Mill site at Pitlochry in April last year.

Tayside health bosses were told yesterday that ownership of the vacant hospital site was split between NHS Tayside and charity trustees.

The hospital has been declared surplus to requirements, but the involvement of charitable trustees has caused a delay in putting the site on the market.

An estimated figure of £300,000 is included in NHS Tayside's forecast of receipts from the sale of the property but it was unclear yesterday when that estimate was obtained and how realistic that might be now.

A paper before members of NHS Tayside's strategic policy and resources committee meeting in King's Cross Hospital, Dundee, yesterday stated the site has attracted interest from a housing association and may be sold during the financial year starting next month.

"There was a slight delay because of endowments involvement in the site", said NHS Tayside's financial controller for service development.

The· committee was told that the endowments trustees had now agreed joint marketing disposal of the site.

The financial controller said endowments trustees had around 40% interest in the site. They had recommended sale of the site as a whole.

"We are making a formal request to the board (of NHS Tayside) for the disposal of the site if that is possible in the current economic climate."

The committee members agreed to recommend to the board the disposal of the site.

The disused hospital was identified earlier this year as a possible prison site.

The Tory justice spokesman wrote to every health board in Scotland to ask if they had any unused premises that could be potentially turned into secure accommodation.

NHS Tayside identified Irvine Memorial Hospital in Pitlochry and the former Armitstead Child Development Centre on Monifieth Road, Broughty Ferry.

2014

24th July 2014 – Proposal for Ex-Hospital

A disused Pitlochry Hospital faces being demolished.

Plans have been submitted to Perth & Kinross Council that would see the former Irvine Memorial Hospital torn down to make way for private housing.

2018

December 2018 – Change of Name

Since the opening of this project, the Dementia Unit no longer exists and sits empty. The meals, which were initially brought from Aberfeldy Hospital by road, are now prepared and made in the kitchen of Pitlochry Community Hospital as the Aberfeldy Hospital was closed in 2017.

The kitchen in Pitlochry Community Hospital was always there and well-equipped, but it was claimed by NHS Tayside they were unable to provide staff to Pitlochry. The centralising of other facilities in Pitlochry also seems to have failed to materialise, as many clinics and follow-up appointments are in Perth or Ninewells.

The new Pitlochry Community Hospital and GP surgery is light, airy, and warm, but has poor access; the only road is via a single lane bridge under the railway, and then twists and turns down to the hospital and can be difficult in winter. The parking is limited and often at busy time's cars queue up to park in the few bays provided. In the winter, if not in a car, the access via the road or Burnside is dark and lonely, and fairly steep for anyone with health problems such as walking, breathing or heart complaints. However, there are buses.

Overall, there were few areas capable of accommodating the area required for the complex. It was felt that the name of the Irvine Memorial Hospital could not be kept, and the Americanised Community Hospital was used; one illogical reason the NHS gave for the name was that Irvine Memorial Hospital misled visitors to think of Irvine in Ayrshire. Therefore, the locals had to accept the new name and Dr William Irvine has been put into the past.

CHAPTER SIX

Memories and Staff Experiences of the Irvine Memorial Hospital and the Various Hospital Units

IRVINE MEMORIAL HOSPITAL

It's the Thought that Counts

IT WAS LAMBING TIME, and this young shepherd lad – about twenty years old – came in with an arm injury which wasn't healing. He was a nice friendly lad and responded well to a week's tender loving care. His arm healed and he was discharged. A week later, a lovely bouquet of spring flowers was delivered by the florist, for the staff from the shepherd laddie. He was leaving the area. A while later, a bill arrived from the florist for the flowers. He had forgotten to pay for them! The nursing staff didn't mind; they had enjoyed having him as a patient.

A Doctor's View

I came in 1953 and at that time Irvine Memorial Nursing Home was a sort of 'L' shape. The North wing of the 'U' at the entrance had not been built. This had certain consequences. The only waiting room for visitors and out-patients attending clinics was a large bench on the right side of the front hall. It could be quite crowded.

At that time the present consulting room was a large broom cupboard and a dry goods store, and there was room at the end of this for clinic out-patients to undress and dress again. The actual consulting was done in the X-ray room as there was room for an examination couch at the side of the X-ray machine. Casualties waited in the theatre ante-room and were dealt with in the theatre. A flow of casualties in the middle of an out-patient consulting session caused a considerable traffic problem for the nursing staff!

The present day-room was the nurses' dining room and sitting room, and there was no day room at that time. Ambulant patients just had to stay in the ward or walk the corridor. The present day-room was constituted by Mrs Arnie, the matron, in the 1970s.

In 1953, the matron was Miss Howie, a really splendid woman, who seemed to be permanently on duty. She had been appointed before the war but had gone off as an army nurse (QUARANC) during the war and returned to after the war. She lived on the premises and the present office was a sitting room with a bedroom off it. Not only did she run a very efficient unit, but she was always good-humoured and had a natural dignity. Living on the premises meant she was always available – bad for her but good for us.

She even took emergency X-rays for the doctors; a time-consuming procedure which we had to do ourselves after she retired. Her able henchman was Sister Dott along with a night sister. She was a great character. I remember Sister Dott was expecting a male admission, and finding a man in the hall, she got him undressed and into a bed despite his protestations before discovering that he was waiting for an out-patient appointment.

At that time, girls leaving school at sixteen or seventeen and intending to become nurses could come to IMNH as auxiliaries before going to PRI at eighteen for full training. Sadly, it soon stopped as it was felt they were too young to cope with the nursing of dying patients. Ours were very well chaperoned and counselled by Miss Howie and seemed to enjoy it and came to no psychological harm. We felt the practical nursing and tender loving care they were taught was of great benefit when they went to a teaching hospital, which was much more impersonal.

The NHS started in July 1948 and PRI became fully staffed with consultants. Prior to that, many operations were done in IMH. Professor Alexander of Dundee would come over to do an appendix or hernia repairs, with the local GP giving the anaesthetic. Mr F. Martin came from Edinburgh to do tonsillectomies. After 1948 all major surgery was done in PRI although we did some minor surgery at IMNH using a rather antiquated anaesthetic machine. The development of modern theatres and anaesthesiology inevitably rightly stopped this.

Dr Christopher Grant, GP (1953-88 – d. 1st April 2018)

Tales from an Auxiliary Nurse

I was just seventeen years old when I came down to work at the Irvine. I stayed in the nurses' quarters as home was in Dulnain Bridge. The nurses' rooms were small, very basically furnished, and cold. The windows opened only a little way at the top and bottom, to make sure no-one could climb in or out! There were five or six rooms, some of them occupied by agency nurses who covered night shifts. Despite the fact that hours were long – we worked split shifts, and there never seemed to be enough to eat – we enjoyed our work and had a lot of laughs. Kate Robertson, one of the staff nurses, often invited us to her house on a Saturday for a good meal; we looked forward to that. Nellie Scott was the matron then. She lived in too but had her own sitting room and bathroom. Matron's shoes squeaked, which meant we always knew where she was.

We worked hard – I remember scraping off old floor polish with a knife before putting on new polish – but we didn't mind. It was a good place to work in and the patients had good care. I have very happy memories of my time there.

Margaret Rose, nursing auxiliary (1965-71)

Reflections of a Chaplain

A main feature of the Nursing Home is its friendliness. *"It's like a home from home"*, was a general comment from visitors, relatives, and patients.

As chaplain, I was accepted readily as part of a team and that was a privilege which I appreciated, though often felt that I received more encouragement and inspiration than I was ever able to give. The examples of courage, cheerfulness and contentment shown by many long-stay patients is clear on my memory. The Nursing Home provided me with an immediate awareness of spiritual values at many practical levels, which is not to be forgotten.

Christmas was always a special time in the hospital. Flora Donaldson used to bring a group of Sunday School children to sing carols, sometimes accompanied by percussion instruments. They gathered in the darkened corridors with coloured lights reflecting from the Christmas decorations. The older folks in particular always enjoyed the children's voices and the telling of the Christmas story.

It was always thought to introduce more regular entertainment. This idea met with general approval. Music, song, and humour were regarded as good forms of therapy. Everyone who was asked to take part was very willing to do so. Nothing seemed to be too much trouble for the staff who co-operated with enthusiasm in all these extras.

Revd Frank Martin, Chaplain (1973-91)

Another Chaplain's View
My time as chaplain was marked by an ever-growing respect for the caring nursing offered the dying. What was offered was far more than the basic medicine of pain control and clean sheets. There was the kindness of a community of care; the encouragement of comforting words at critical moments; and, above all, the understanding and respect for people of all kinds and in all situations. How fortunate they were there to experience the friendship and care of the local cottage hospital.

The Reverend Bill Shannon (chaplain, 1991-1998).

Small Beginnings – 'The Friends'

Patients and relatives of patients have always been very generous to our hospital and back in the mid-60s, Elspeth Grant, wife of Dr Willie Grant, became concerned that there was no organisation in place to oversee the spending of this money. She invited Audrey Grant and Ann Martin to form with her a small committee to work with the hospital staff to choose equipment and 'extras', not provided by the Health Board, for the benefit of the patients. Meeting in each other's homes, this committee was the 'small beginning' of what later became the Friends of Irvine Memorial.

In 1979, Dr Willie Grant retired, and he and his wife left Pitlochry. The committee was joined by Margo Ross, and later by Jenny Cruikshank and Marion White. Eventually, in 1979, the Friends of Irvine Memorial Hospital was born, and formally constituted in 1979. As the committee grew, so did the membership of the 'Friends', and the many donations received, showing how much the people of this area appreciate the care given by *'our'* hospital.

Ann Martin, past Chairman of 'The Friends'

A Matron Remembers

I first saw the Irvine Memorial Hospital when I was invited to attend for the forthcoming vacancy of matron. I was most impressed with my first sight of the building, the lovely gardens, and the general appearance of the hospital. It looked like a nice comfortable family home, and it proved to be that. There was a feeling of friendliness – I was immediately made welcome; and when I was offered the post, I had no hesitation in confirming my acceptance. I felt it was right for me – despite doubts expressed by some friends and colleagues that I would be bored, that I would rusticate. How wrong people can be. I gained more experience in nursing care and ancillary duties than I had in five years at my previous post in an acute unit of 120 beds. It was a challenge I looked forward to. A new unit was to be commissioned in the very near future – that was exciting.

The staff, patients and indeed their relatives felt they had a stake in the hospital and were always willing to proffer help and advice on how things should be done. On many occasions, I was grateful for this local knowledge which helped me through difficult situations; and saved me from making avoidable mistakes. Everyone with who I came in contact was willing to help; and loyalty from all grades of staff was never in short supply. We had sad times, traumatic times, and happy times. We worked in stressful situations and usually we got through them and could come out smiling.

We had lots of fun. I recall the weekend we moved the GP Unit to the new Atholl Ward, as the GP Unit was getting a complete refurbishment. Staff and their families gave up their Saturday evening to help us 'flit'. Everything was going like clockwork and about 8pm we thought we could safely move all the chairs from the Out Patients Department. We had just done this when a busload of tourists, who had been involved in an accident, arrived. Alas, we had no seats or trolleys for them. The furniture removers were none too pleased to have to reset Out Patients Department. Everything had to be brought back. There were many amusing incidents.

Where would you find a handyman willing to come on duty at 6am to clear deep snow from the hospital entrance? At Irvine Memorial Hospital of course.

Where would you find staff who thought nothing of coming to work by tractor, in wild weather conditions, and arriving cold and wet but cheerful all the way from Enochdhu? At Irvine Memorial Hospital of course.

Irvine Memorial Hospital played a big part in my life for more than twelve happy years. I loved being part of the hospital family. It was a privilege to work there. I worked with very many caring, committed, and interesting people from whom I learned a great deal.

Ruby Ripley, Matron (1977-89)

Views of a Handyman

The snow had fallen hard all night, so by the time I set off for work 1½ hours earlier than usual, there was eighteen inches of snow along the pavements. There were no footprints in front of me. At the hospital, the priority was to clear the front door for traffic. Once that channel was clear, I set about clearing the staff car parking spaces so that, by the time the nurses who had managed to get through the deep snow arrived, there were some bays for them to park in. Footpaths and the entrance to out-patients were next to be cleared, although the snow fell steadily all day. My work was never really done that day.

Archie Currie, handyman

A9 Emergencies
In the early days – between 1978 and 1996 – we catered for all accidents on the old A9 between the County boundary and the new Jubilee Bridge just north of Dunkeld, and into the hills as far as Fealar. There was no Pitlochry by-pass. No compulsory wearing of seat-belts (lots of cars didn't have any and lots of folks didn't like wearing them!) No specially fitted ambulances. No paramedics.

Trained nurses were called in as ambulance escorts when patients' conditions were critical. You could be working in the garden, called in, changed into uniform and en route to PRI within fifteen minutes – having abandoned garden, home, family – the hospital always came first! That did not mean that the care was not first class. Our doctors belonged to BASICS and were well in touch with all that went on in the forefront of 'Accident and Emergency' treatment, for example, on the night of the Lockerbie disaster, bags were packed here in Irvine Memorial Hospital and taken by our doctors who were on standby in case there turned out to be a large number of casualties – they were never needed.

Veronica Charity, nursing sister, 1978-96

Activities involving Staff and Patients
The Square Ball Team, the winners presented by Matron Ruby Ripley with a cardboard urinal covered in tinfoil: 'The Belles of St Trinian's'. A few high blood pressures would have been taken that day amongst the male patients. A 'Fashion Show' in the garden with patients and visitors as audience. Nurses and other staff modelling. A Burns Night, Christmas flings, St Andrew Nights with a Clootie, and more – all giving patients and staff enjoyment and memories of happy times.

THE GENERAL PRACTITIONER UNIT AND OTHER UNITS OF IRVINE MEMORIAL HOSPITAL

The General Practioner Unit
This unit served patients served patients from around the locality. This included a wide variety of conditions and ailments, from semi-acute illnesses post-operative care, rehabilitation to palliative and terminal care. The purpose of the ward was to provide a safe and caring environment where the emphasis was placed on providing high quality care for the patient as an individual. The aim was to provide care and interventions that would enable patients to return home where possible; or to facilitate suitable placement for their future care; or to provide a peaceful and dignified end to their lives when no further treatments were possible.

To achieve these aims, a multidisciplinary team worked together, with these being nurses, doctors, occupational therapists, physiotherapists, Social Services, and any other agency required to help the needs of patients.

The Atholl Unit
In 2001, this unit was refurbished from a ward for frail-elderly continuing care to a dementia assessment unit. In April of that year, an 'Open Day' was held when around 100 local people attended, which was an enjoyable day. Both the staff and patients were delighted with the refurbishment and felt it was more like a hotel.

District Nurses
Thirty-five years ago, district nursing also helped in taking over the care of patients from the hospital once they returned home, or the patients visited the nurses' station, which was in a small annex of a house across from Scotland's Hotel. It was cold and had very little space. The adjoining room was used by physiotherapists, speech therapists, and was also the Baby Clinic. Fortunately, paperwork was almost non-existent therefore leaving room for essential equipment.

At that time 'On-Call' (that was introduced later) was not in use which was fortunate as the health board cars were given almost more consideration than the nurses'. As nurses living outside Pitlochry were not allowed to take the car home – it had to be garaged in Pitlochry, in one of Fishers Hotel's private lock-ups – the health board paid the bill.

Mornings were spent getting daily patients washed and dressed; there were weekly baths. New mums and babies had to be seen as soon as possible. Dressings were attended to – no latex gloves, but good hand-washing regimes were always adhered to. The types of dressings used on wounds were limited; over the years they have greatly increased making district nurses' work easier, but their work was and always will be one of carer and friend to the people in their care.

Betty Watson, district nurse

Ward Pets
IMH had a fish tank which was donated by Perth Aquarium Society and filled by fish by them. They came every two – three months and cleaned out the tank and re-stocked the tank if needed. They also spent time talking to patients stimulating an interest in the fish.

At one time there were love birds, but they proved to be too active and chatty, therefore too much to cope with! The budgies provided a lot of pleasure and were tended by Willie Christie. A dog visitor attended when his mistress did the flowers. He was a great favourite with one patient and was found under their bed when he had run away from home, possibly chasing a female in heat!

The Garden
Affleck Gray, author of *The Big Grey Man of Ben Macdhui* and *Legends of the Cairngorms*, was a great support in the garden, advising on plants, advising on potatoes *"to clean the ground"* instead of using weed-killer, then lifting mature potatoes of different varieties and colours, showing them to patients and having them for supper.

Affleck visited the wards and spoke of his adventures in the Cairngorms periodically going outside for a puff on his pipe. He went on to design the Sensory Garden, the land for which was acquired from Castlebeigh Hotel, situated just behind the hotel. It was laid out for wheelchairs, simmers, and on occasion a moveable bed, to be pushed round. The senses of hearing, sight, smell, touch, and taste were all there, as well as a summer house.

Schoolchildren helped to maintain the garden as well as wheeling patients along the corridors. The schoolchildren also made the models for the nativity which were used for years. Many young folk went to the hospital so that they could learn about caring: from the playgroup with their nativity plays, Rainbows with bowls of crocus bulbs, Brownies, Guides, to Duke of Edinburgh Award candidates who often did stints of three to six months coming in on Sunday mornings for an hour to make beds and talk to patients.

Some children built up relationships with long-term patients, on one occasion two eight-year-old boys standing in silent admiration of a patient who had just become 100 – she was reciting poetry she had learned at school. The children wrote letters and made cards; friendships were made across the generations. Patients smiled, eyes twinkled as memories came back, with fingers and toes tapping as the children sang and entertained.

Students

Students undertaking a Diploma in Public Health visited from Dundee 'to see a small community hospital'. They mostly came from Third World countries and many from Africa. On one occasion, a patient's husband attended on the students' visit. They were thrilled when he greeted them in their own language – but were amazed when Dr Kennedy arrived on the ward and talked to them about his parents' time in Zambia and then they met a patient from Dunkeld who spoke about his time in West Africa. This demonstrated the diversity of people who have been a part of IMH.

A Thank You Poem

I am very well looked after here
By the doctor and nurses so dear
They appear to be happy all the time
Nothing to help is trouble to them
Good attention and so tasty food
We are lucky with a hospital so good
I am sleeping well and walk without pain
Sun gently sets as cleared is the rain
Everyone here so jolly and kind
The best of hospitals you can find

May Scott - Patient

CHAPTER SEVEN

The Ambulance Service, Toberargan Surgery, Doctors and Chemists in the Atholl Area, Senior Nursing Staff, the Irvine Memorial Hanging, Tablecloths

AN IMPORTANT AID TO HOSPITALS is the ambulance service. This service dates back to the early nineteenth century and was called by the French *hospital ambulant*, or walking hospital, which refers to the treatment of the wounded on a battlefield – the name ambulance came from this.

The ambulance service we know today started in 1945, when Air Raid Precaution ambulances (left over from the Second World War) were put into use. They were later replaced through public service subscription and taken over by the NHS in 1948.

In 1949, Pitlochry's ambulance was stationed in a garage next door to a retail premises which was once the 'Bakers Oven' (derelict in 2019). The mechanics there maintained it. In 1970, the Scottish Ambulance Service took on the contract, but the ambulance was still based at the garage; and three more ambulance staff were recruited, so there was still just one person to each vehicle. If a patient was seriously ill or injured, a nurse from Irvine Memorial Hospital would accompany the driver when transporting a patient to PRI or Ninewells.

At that time. casualties numbered about 30 a month on the old A9 – Dalnaspidal to Dowally section – and these were initially treated at Irvine Memorial Hospital by its doctors, who decided where patients should go for further treatment if needed.

In 1974, a new ambulance station was built in Kennedy Place, off Higher Oakfield, overlooking the play park that still stands there today. The building is currently a veterinary practice.

In 1980, a campaign – 'Save a Life' promoted by the BBC, saw local GPs and ambulance workers holding workshops in Pitlochry to teach the local populace how to perform 'Cardiac Pulmonary Resuscitation'.

This brought the people of Pitlochry to realise a defibrillator was needed. Fund raising in 1980 by local Pitlochry folk, raised money to provide a machine, which was presented to the Irvine Memorial Hospital that year.

The year 1984 saw an increase in ambulance staff that allowed each vehicle to be double-staffed. This made the work of transporting patients to clinics at PRI slightly easier. Nonetheless, even when carrying a full load of patients for clinics, if an ambulance came across an accident on the A9, it would stop to deal with the incident. The ambulance would not continue to PRI for the clinics until another ambulance arrived to take care of the accident casualties, so patients were sometimes late for out-patient appointments. In 1984, the service was split, and the Patient Transfer Service was formed, allowing the Ambulance Service to concentrate on accidents and emergencies.

In 1991, Tayside Health Board decided there was a need for para-medics: ambulance workers with specialised training, which required a 10-week training course in Glasgow. Once trained, the paramedics underwent a change of uniform to green overalls, which were more comfortable and easier to work in.

When the Irvine Memorial Hospital was at the top of Nursing Home Brae, the ambulance had to descend very gently to the main road as the Brae is very steep. The ambulance station is today at the rear of Pitlochry Community Hospital in the Bobbin Mill area on Ferry Road.

Toberargan Surgery
In the past, many GPs held surgeries in their own homes. Patients chose the GP they wanted to consult, and often a patient would just appear at the GP's house during surgery times, or, if a telephone was available, a patient would ring, which was usually attended to by the GP's wife or housekeeper, who acted as secretary, telephonist, receptionist, as well as cleaner and housewife. On arrival, a patient calling at the GP's house may have sat in the hall or lounge for their turn/appointment. When GPs joined up and formed a joint practice, it was likely to have been a great relief to their wives or housekeepers to have their home to themselves.

Toberargan Surgery, which opened in 1971, was set up by Dr William Grant ('Goatie') and Dr Trevor Ross, both GPs in Atholl. Dr Grant lived at Croft-na-Coille, Toberargan Road, and kept goats in the part of his garden that he later gave over for the surgery to be built on. Dr Grant had kept goats as his wife had a skin problem and the goats' milk was a help. Dr Ross played a main role in the planning and designing of the surgery. By the time Dr Ross retired in 1995, three major extensions had been added.

Toberargan Surgery sat at the base of the hill leading up to the Irvine Memorial Hospital. However, because the surgery was located at the junction of three roads, parking, pick-ups, and drop-offs were difficult. When more doctors joined the practice along with nurses and clerical staff, parking became a big problem; as was accommodation for all the extra staff in the surgery. Consequently, by the late 1990s, a bigger surgery was needed. So, when in 2008 the Irvine Memorial Hospital and other facilities in Pitlochry moved to the Bobbin Mill location, the surgery also moved.

Doctors and Chemists in the Atholl Area

Doctors

W. S. Irvine	1833-93	D. A. Cruikshank	1978-2008
R. Irvine	1876-97	M. Faulds	1979-97
J. Beattie	1891-1914/16	D. S. Kennedy	1988-2017
J. Anderson	1894-1934	D. P. Leaver	1990-
A. Biden	1920-47	J. I. R. McHugh	1995-
— Newton	1925-44	G. W. McCrory	1997-2010
— McCarone	1940-58		
— Hayes	1944-48	**Chemists**	
— Henderson	1947-69	Mr R. Gellatly, Main Street,	
T. & A. Robinson	1948-52	Pitlochry	
— Thom	1950-79	Mr W. Robertson, Main Street,	
W. Grant	1952-79	Pitlochry	
C. Grant	1953-88	*(A Perth dentist attended periodically*	
R. T. Ross	1969-95	*at the chemists)*	

Senior Nursing Staff

The following is an incomplete list of matrons and other senior nurses who worked at Irvine Memorial Hospital.

1901   1st District Nurse – Miss Anderson
              23rd November: Mrs McIntyre was appointed Matron (no
              record of appointment being taken up). First Matron was
              likely to have been Mrs Bell.

1911   February: A probationer Assistant Matron was appointed.

1916-17   Courtier Dutton was appointed as Matron along with a
              probationer nurse, Miss McEachnie.

1919   Sister Jean McGibbon Campbell was appointed Matron.
              Under the French flag, she received the Croix de Guerre. She
              also nursed in the United States (St Albans).

1920   A qualified maternity nurse, Christina Stewart, was
              appointed Matron. She resided at Catherine Bank, Pitlochry.
              A new district nurse was also appointed.

1922   Christina Stewart died.

1929   January: Miss MacGregor Stewart resigned to open a
              convalescent home at Craigroyston.

1933   Miss Lawrence was appointed Matron. Mrs Dow of Tomcroy
              was the district nurse.

1953   Miss Howie (who had been an Army Nurse – QUARANC)
              and Sister Duff in position.

1955   Matron Jean McGibbon Campbell died aged 70.

1965   Nellie Scott was Matron. Miss (Helen or Jean) Scott was
              Matron for ten years.

1970   Mrs Arnie was Matron.

1977   Ruby Ripley was Matron.

AFTER 1989

              Robert Lister was senior nursing officers. Subsequently,
              Muriel Lynd, Pitlochry and Aberfeldy, was senior nursing
              officer.

Tablecloths

On her retirement as Matron on her sixtieth birthday on 22nd October
1989, Ruby Ripley was given a gift of two signed tablecloths by the staff
of the Irvine Memorial Hospital. The embroidery on the signatures was
made by Isobel McGregor, now in Balhousie Care Home.

The signatures on the smaller tablecloth are detailed in Table A
(overleaf); those on the large tablecloth in Table B. *(page 178)*

The Irvine Memorial Hanging

The Irvine Memorial Hanging is a large embroidery (7'4" x 4') made by
Rural Institute women (SWRI) and a few friends for the Irvine Memorial
Hospital. The hanging is now in the entrance to Pitlochry Community
Hospital. A booklet about the hanging is available in the hospital.

The Irvine Memorial Hanging.

TABLE A

C. Bannatyne	EN	Mary Mclaren	NA
Catriona Bridges	S	Sheila McLauchlan	NA
E. Bruce	C	Cath Megaughin	NA
Helen Cameron	NA	Jeannie Melloy	
H. Campbell	SN	Anne Michie	NA
Jenny Carson	S	Maureen Munro	C
Veronica Charity	S	Lynne O'Neal	
Cheryl Davis	NA	Lorna Pointer	S
Margaret S. Dickson	NA	Margaret Preston	AW
Charlotte Dingwall	NA	Sheena Rae	NA
Kathleen Duncan	EN	Susan Rae	NA
Margaret Duncan	NA	Cynthia Ringrose	OT
M Fullarton	NA	Eve C. Ritchie	NA
Dorothy Gent	SN	Ann Robertson	NA
Doris Graham	C	Betsy Saint	NA
May Hood	NA	Jessie Seaton	NA
Bobby Hubbard	NA	Martha Seaton	AW
Marie Kennedy	C	Nan Sneddon	AW
Jean Kirby	NA	Ann Shields	SN
Francis J. Lauder	S	Jane Smith	NA
Irene Lees	NA	C. Strain	NA
Isobel McGregor	NA	Barbara Urquhart	AW
Catriona McKay	SN	Margaret Urquhart	AW

AD:	Ambulance Driver	HS:	Hospital Secretary
AW:	Auxiliary Worker	NA:	Nursing Auxiliary
C:	Cook	OT:	Occupational Therapist
CT:	Consultant	PH:	Physiotherapist
DN:	District Nurse	PM:	Practice Manager
DR:	Doctor	S:	Sister
EN:	Enrolled Nurse	SN:	Staff Nurse
HC:	Hospital Chaplin	SR:	Surgery Receptionist
HJ:	Hospital Janitor		

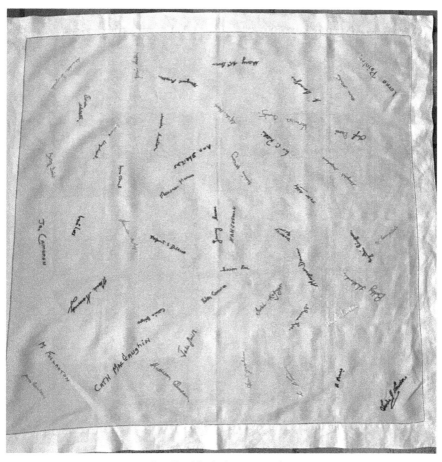

Small tablecloth presented to
Matron Ruby Ripley on her retirement, 1989.

TABLE B

Name	Code	Name	Code	Name	Code
Geoff Allen	AD	Margaret Fullarton	NA	Maureen Munroe	C
Janet Baird	C	Valerie Gallacher	SN	Louise Murray	C
Chrissie Bannatyne	EN	Norma Gammie	SN	Jeannette Paterson	C
Rosemary Banner		Pam Gashin	SN	Joan Pirie	
David Bilsland	Dr	James Geldart	AD	Lorna Pointer	S
Mary Brabury		Jane Gemell		Margaret Preston	AW
John Brennan	CT	Dorothy Gent	SN	Gladys Proudfoot	S
David J. Bruce	AD	Doris Graham	C	Louise R.	C
Elizabeth Bruce	C	Christopher Grant	DR	Sheena Rae	NA
Catriona Bridges	S	Carol Hamilton	AW	Susan Rae	NA
Gordon Bryson		Jenny Hill	PM	Margaret Rattray	SN
Helen Cameron	NA	May Hood	NA	Anne Reid	C
Jo Cameron	NA	Bobby Hubbard	NA	Melanie Ringrose	SN
Helen Campbell	SN	Cynthia Hunter	EN	Eve Ritchie	NA
Moira Campbell	S	Jan Hynd	SR	Ann Robertson	NA
Judith Carruthers	NA	Allan Jamieson	AD	Eilidh Robertson	EN
Jenny Carson	S	Marian Jardine	C	Rita Robertson	NA
Ann Castle	OT	Lynne Jones	SN	Trevor Ross	DR
Alice Charity	NA	Douglas S. Kennedy	DR	Aileen Rough	
Veronica Charity	S	Mairi Kennedy	NA	Amy Rowley	
Christine Cheape	DN	Marie F. T. Kennedy	C	Betsy Saint	NA
Anne Clark	C	Jean Kirby	NA	David Saunders	AD
Martha Collins		Alison Kirk	SN	Jessie Seaton	NA
David A. Cruikshank	DR	Helen Lang	NA	Martha Seaton	AW
Archibald Currie	J	Louise Lauder	S	Bill Shannon	HC
Cathy Daleymount	SN	Irene Lees	NA	Ann Shields	SN
Mary Dalglish		M. Lawson	SN	Jane Smith	NA
Mary Dalziel	PH	Johan MacDonald	NA	Julia Smith	SN
J. Davidson	C	Isobel McGregor	NA	Jean Symons	
Cheryl Davis	NA	Kenneth Macveal		Celia Talbot	S
Leslie Derby	C	G.D. Majinder	DR	B. Urquhart	AW
Margaret S. Dickson	NA	Robert Manz	AD	M. Urquhart	AW
J. Donald	CT	Frank Martin	HC	Morag Uytman	DN
Sheila Dunbar	OT	Kay McGuire		Betty Watson	DN
Margaret Drysdale	SN	Catriona McKay	SN	Margaret Watson	
Jim Duffy	AD	Pat McKenzie	SR	Sandra Webster	HS
Kathy Duncan	EN	Mary McLaren	NA	John Weir	
Margaret Duncan	NA	Sheila McLauchlan	NA	Ivy Wensley	SN
Yvonne Duncan		Ali McRae	AD	Caroline White	C
Lorna Duthie		Ann Michie	NA	Bertie Wood	CT
Marion Faulds	DR	Audrey Milne	NA		
Christine Fulton	SN	Fiona Mitchell			

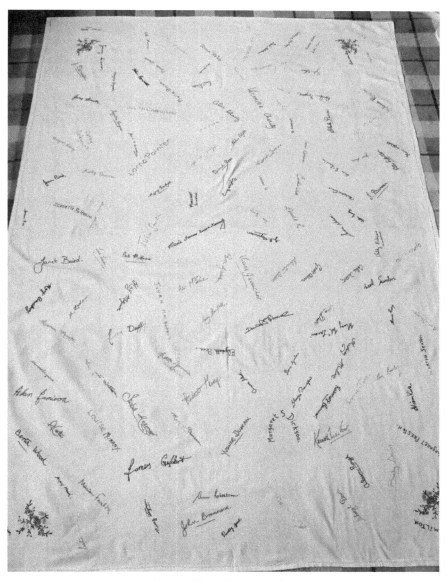

Large tablecloth presented to
Matron Ruby Ripley on her retirement, 1989.

CHAPTER EIGHT

Chequers Residential Care Home, the Tryst Day Centre, Perthshire Senior Citizens Good Neighbourhood Association, and Bobbin Mill

CHEQUERS RESIDENTIAL CARE HOME
A Service of Thanksgiving for Chequers
24th November 1966 – 21st January 2009
Pitlochry, Church of Scotland

Sunday 18th January 2009 at 3 pm
Welcome
Call to Worship

HYMN 166 (Slane, 500)
Lord of all hopefulness, Lord of all joy

Prayers of Approach
To be led by Revd David-Court,
Convenor of Social Care Council (CrossReach)

Eternal God, into the peace of your presence we bring our restless lives. Down through the ages men and women have sought you and found that your faithfulness has no end. Your people long ago journeyed by your guidance and rested on your love. So, guide us as a pillar of cloud by day, and tire by night, that our imaginations may be filled with your beauty, our minds be fired by your truth, and our hearts be overflowing with your love; for without you life has no source, or purpose, or destiny. Refresh our faith, restore our confidence, and lay your guiding hand on our lives. We ask this through Jesus Christ our Lord.

Merciful God, we know that in our lives there have been some wrong things that we should not have done; and some good things that we have left undone. Forgive us; grant us your peace; and give us the strength to start again to respond to your call to live your way, with Jesus' help.

Eternal God, as we step forward into the unknown future make us brave and courageous and help us put our trust in you. Give us a sense of fellowship with the saints of every age, and may we encourage all who journey with us in this life of faith. We ask all this in the name of Jesus Christ our Lord. Amen.

Scripture Readings
Micah 6:6-8,
to be read by Elspeth Finlay, Unit Manager,
Chequers, 2005- 2009
Mark 8:34-38,
to be read by Alastair Dickson, gardener, and volunteer driver at
Chequers, 2003-2009

Anthem by Choir
Gloria, gloria, in excelsis Deo! (CH4 760)

Some Memories of Chequers
Dr David Cruikshank, GP with responsibility for health and care
of residents of Chequers, 1978-2008 and Euan Martin,
son of Revd Frank and Mrs Anne Martin

Introduction
Chequers Eventide Home, Chequers Residential Home, Chequers Church of Scotland, or just simply Chequers as it is known affectionately in this community and also nationwide, all names that seem to have been attached to the Chequers many have known at some time or other for its 42 years existence – a family home providing care for many residents over the years and an integral part in the local care of the community plan.

Chequers the building, Chequers the people and Chequers and the community.

Share with me some memories and reflections of those 42 years:

Chequers – the Building

An approach regarding an Eventide Home in the Presbytery of Dunkeld came around 1964 when a strong case was made for having such a home within the bounds. When the Committee on Social Service had agreed to co-operate, there came on the market the Chequers Private Hotel, which was situated on the main road through Pitlochry – an ideal location – on the flat and within easy reach of the shops. The hotel had been owned by the Burgons who were members of the East Church here in Pitlochry and had put the hotel on the market prior to their move to Fort William. After examination the property was purchased, complete with furnishings, for £30,000 with vacant possession on 22nd September 1965. A Promotion Committee was set up to raise funds for the project and, meantime, estimates were procured for the reconstruction and extension of the building to make it suitable to accommodate thirty-one persons.

The cost of alterations amounted to £25,382, a much larger figure than had at first been expected, and the Home was ready by 24th November 1966, for the opening ceremony.

Chequers Residential Care Home, 1966-2009.

An extension to Chequers was opened on 6th August 1980. This allowed increased accommodation to make a home for 37 residents. The lounge and dining room was enlarged and improved, a quiet room and TV room was made possible and new staff accommodation was constructed at the rear of the building. The availability of 12-day care places was welcomed, as a very much-required community need.

The garden was devotedly cared for by many gardeners over the years – letting the residents have somewhere to sit and enjoy many aspects of God's creation.

It was also a focus point and contact with the rest of the world. The frequent trains on their journeys North and South – the very frequent passing motor traffic but most importantly the passing visitors and community members who would stop by for a blether. The placing of a council seat outside Chequers encouraged people to stop and share a chat with the residents.

Residents were encouraged to bring their own small personal possessions when they came to Chequers and many still grace the walls – many other artifacts were made and donated – the lectern used each Sunday at the service was given by the former East Church Sunday School.

Chequers and its People

The main instigators behind the thought of requiring an eventide home in Pitlochry were the Revd Harold Meredith of Tenandry and the Revd Frank Martin of the East Church in Pitlochry. Both played an integral role in seeing Chequers created despite considerable initial local community and central church committee opposition, many frustrations and delays with planners, and builders.

It was opened in the East Church, Pitlochry, by one who had given outstanding service to the Committee on Social Service, namely, Mrs. Helen C. Sutherland, MBE, Wemyss Bay. The Home was dedicated by the Revd Andrew M. M. Giles, Joint Vice Convener of the Social and Moral Welfare Board, and the Revd H. M. Ricketts, Convener of the Social and Moral Welfare Board, presided; while others taking part were the Revd H. A. Wright, minister of Moulin and Pitlochry West Church; the Revd Harold Meredith, Moderator of the Presbytery of Dunkeld, the Revd Kenneth MacVicar, Clerk of the Presbytery of Dunkeld; and Dr J. S. Sutherland, Provost of Pitlochry.

The dedication and opening of the new extension was carried out on 6th August 1980 by The Very Revd Professor Robin Barbour – the Moderator of the 1997 General Assembly – whose family had long connections with the home and of course still lives locally at Fincastle.

The Revd Frank Martin – the home's chaplain – led the support of the people of Atholl and a local committee had as its first Convener, the Revd H. Meredith, Tenandry, and Dr Neil D. Fraser, Pitlochry, was its first Secretary.

The Local Committee as it was known at that time had representatives from every Church in the Presbytery from as far afield as Killin, Glen Lyon and Kinloch Rannoch and was there in support to the staff and residents and organized fundraising for the home. In a way in addition their duties were then somewhat simplistic – monthly visitation and inspection of menus were the norm.

The local Committee now known as the Circle of Friends and still made up of local representatives of the churches and communities has continued to meet regularly and support the residents and staff in many ways.

Very soon after it was opened, the Home was filled, and the residents found in Chequers a place of serenity and comfort – a central focus within the community.

Chequers did not cater exclusively for people in the immediate vicinity of Pitlochry, but most residents did come from local towns and villages. The presence of Chequers as far as possible let elderly people be kept within their own community. It also provided a much welcome resource for residents of the community who were able to bring relatives in need of care to somewhere close at hand to them. Many of us here have had experience of that most welcome help.

The staff gave residents 24 hours a day, superlative care.

The first matron and superintendent – Mr and Mrs Munro – moved within ten months of the opening of Chequers to Oban and were replaced by Ruth and John Boa to whom we are indebted for considerable factual information used in the preparation of this service. They stayed for 36 years and retired after giving the most faithful and dedicated service. Ruth and John were synonymous with Chequers and all it has meant to so many over its existence. In turn, they were succeeded by Cathie Cairns and more recently Elspeth Finlay.

The now known as 'unit manager' led a team of dedicated staff who cared and provided for every need of each individual resident – all of us who have been involved in one way or other with Chequers will remember the characters who made up that resident family of Chequers – some more demanding than others – some frailer than others – some so independent – some resident there for a short time – some for many, many years – however short or long the stay was, it was their home and they were treated as one of that special Chequers family. One resident is remembered as even going youth-hostelling from Chequers aged 80. Special events were celebrated together – Christmas, Easter, World Day of Prayer, Birthdays and national events like Royal Weddings – the residents all got dressed in their finery as if they too were guests – even John and Ruth Boa had their children David and Karen baptized in Chequers – they are with us today.

Many happy relationships were established within the home among residents and staff alike over many years.

Latterly, it was increasingly possible to support the staff in Chequers by involving specialized service providers who visited the residents as needed – the community nurses, the memory nurses, occupational therapists, speech therapists, social care workers and many more members of the Primary Health Care Team.

There are many people throughout those 42 years that have been involved in the success of Chequers and have supported it through difficult and happy times. Many senior Church figures visited – most notable several Moderators of the General Assembly – the last moderator visit in 2007. Key figures in '121' and subsequently Charis House – the Revd Frank Gibson, Joyce Buchanan, and Ian Manson and many more – all the local ministers who took the weekly service in the home – the local community members – the relatives and of course that dedicated band of staff who gave of their all. One cannot mention them all individually – but there was a huge supportive team over the years that gave of their all for the family of Chequers.

There is probably however one person who along with his wife and family made Chequers one of his major priorities in his life and service here in Pitlochry – The Revd Frank Martin.

We are fortunate to have Anne and Frank's family here with us today and I have asked Euan their son to say a few words about his Father's and family involvement in Chequers.

Euan

The year 1966 is well known as the year England won the World Cup, but in our family, the date has much more significance than that. It was the year Chequers opened. This Christmas just past was the first time since 1966 that our family did not have a direct presence to help celebrate Christmas Day with the residents in Chequers. By way of completing the circle, I was very pleased to be asked to say a few words on behalf of the family at today's service.

My dad, Frank Martin, was one of the prime movers behind the idea to provide residential care for older people in the local area. As he recalled in his memoirs, *"The first suggestion to have an eventide home in Pitlochry was made in the Presbytery around 1964. The late Harold Meredith, Minister of Tenandry, and I, were the instigators".*

With good fortune, members of the East Church congregation, the Burgons, placed their hotel on the market at the point when the project was given the go-ahead by the Presbytery and after *"long meetings in Edinburgh"*, Chequers was purchased. Dad goes on to express his frustration at the bureaucracy which seemed to slow the process and states *"I dare say I made myself somewhat unpopular in 121 George Street".* He took some pleasure at being described as *"like a little terrier dog who wouldn't let go"*, but it was this tenacity that ultimately led to the completion of the project within two years – by today's standards, a remarkably quick turnaround from initial concept to the opening of a newly refurbished establishment.

One of my very first memories of Chequers was a wee bit painful, it has to be said. Mum and dad were visiting Ruth and John Boa in their flat at the rear of the building. John, as he was often inclined to do, picked me up and playfully threw me in the air. I can still remember the look of horror on his face as he cracked the Minister's bairn's head off the low ceiling! However, it was nothing a chocolate biscuit and the offer of regular employment couldn't solve. There can't be many people who can say they 'retired' after 25 years of service at the age of 31 years, but that was the situation for me. Every Christmas morning from 1966 onwards until my own family and work commitments intervened, I played Santa, dressed firstly in a red dressing gown and latterly in an oversized Santa suit, with the rest of the family in support helping distribute presents to all the residents. Sadly, the Santa suit fits me now, or rather I fit it, but I still have it, just as we will always have the memories of the warm, caring supportive family environment in Chequers. And of course, it wasn't just at Christmas, there were many happy times throughout the year with parties, Burns Suppers, children's concerts and entertainment from all sorts of local performers like Flora Donaldson and the Happy Harmonicas, or members of the drama group.

In the late 70s, the family connection with Chequers was further strengthened when our granny, dad's mother, spent the last few months of her life as a resident and of course most recently, our mum Ann Martin moved to Chequers when she was no longer able to continue living safely in her own home.

As no doubt others will say, times change, nothing stays the same and the needs of older people require to be met with much higher standards of accommodation than Chequers can now provide. But for the last forty-two years, Chequers has been a community within a community offering security, care and compassion to residents and relatives alike. On behalf of my parents and brother and sister, I would like to say that we are proud to have been involved with Chequers from the outset and privileged to have been part of the Chequers Community.

And now to continue the theme of Community, I'd like to hand you back to Dr Cruikshank.

Chequers and the Community
Chequers stood not only very much at the centre and the heart of this local community but also had contacts with communities and friends worldwide.

Gifts and donations came from all over the world in support of the work done. Not only did Chequers receive but it also gave.

So vital was the shared contribution fostered with groups and people of all ages from the community – pre-school playgroups with the Nativity play, Youth organisations who have held campfires and enrolments in the lounge, pupils undertaking the Duke of Edinburgh Scheme, local school projects, college student placements, community service offenders, student nurses, medical students and young doctors in training – have all given and in return have had their lives influenced by what they saw happening in Chequers through the care and love and expertise of the staff and from their own personal interaction with the residents.

Vital support also came from the Women's Guilds of the local Churches, The Rotary and Round Table Clubs, The Probus and local Masonic Lodge and many more local organisations in providing items of comfort to meet the needs of the residents. But again, in return the staff and residents got themselves involved in fundraising for local and national. projects – Children in Church Care, the local Senior Citizens Bus, The Tryst Day Care project, Radio Heartland, the Meningitis Trust, Cancer Research – just to name a few.

Chequers was a very early pioneer in many fields of social care especially in the use of recall, providing respite and day care growing to a level where the partnership with the Tryst Day Care Centre was vital to meeting the need of care in the community – providing and staffing sixteen places for day care within the extended local community.

Reflections and Thought for the Future
The staff have shared the joys and sorrows of many families and friends of residents over the 42 years that Chequers has been open and in turn staff have found the much-needed support from the local Circle of Friends and the community organisations and individuals, so very willingly and freely given. As the local general practitioner for 30 years, I too, along with my medical colleagues shared many moments of happiness, concern, and sadness in Chequers as the residents came face to face with the diffuse range of illnesses – some simple some often more complex. Many a story could be told but those stories are confidential and will remain my memories and as promised never to be shared or published.

At the service to mark Chequers Silver Jubilee, the hymn *Great is thy Faithfulness* was sung and today that is still so very applicable to all those

189

that have faithfully served Chequers over the last 42 years. We close our service today likewise with that great hymn.

What for the future? Like the other two givers of care in this community the Irvine Memorial Hospital and Toberargan Surgery, there came a time when receivers and providers of medical care realised that the time had come to move on and build anew. Likewise, it had been hoped that Chequers would be part of that new wider vision for an integrated community health care project. Sadly, as we all know, despite intensive negotiations by so many, that is not to be and Chequers will close its doors next week. Some of the present residents have now moved to new accommodations locally and some further afield but only after much individual discussion and relative involvement.

We give thanks that CrossReach however will continue to have an ever presence within this community and beyond – The Tryst Day Centre will still be providing that essential role in care of the community, a small home care service is envisaged to start in the spring and a second new day care centre will open in February at Bankfoot staffed by some of Chequers' team.

Those many folks that have been residents and those that that have been their relatives and friends will be eternally thankful for the support they have received from so many people friends and staff alike. However, what will never be forgotten is the Christian care, love, and devotion that they have received and have seen given by so many staff – those faithful servants of Christ's work.

Although the doors of Chequers will close, and the building sold, let the memories of Chequers live on for us all.

HYMN 736 (Sine Nomine)
Give thanks for life, the measure of our days

Address
'The only things we take with us from our life on earth are
those which we have given away'
Revd Malcolm Ramsay, Chaplain for Chequers, 1998 – 2009

Today we are sharing in a service of Thanksgiving for the life and service of Chequers.

Something we have loved and cherished has come to a close, and today we gather to give thanks for its life, and with sadness, to mark its end.

Sometimes when I visit people to prepare for a funeral service, I tell them that I think there is such a thing as a 'good' funeral. A good funeral has at least three elements. We can look for these both in a service for a human life, and also in a service like this for the life of an institution like Chequers. The three elements are these: thanksgiving, sadness, and faith. Let us think about them in turn and apply them to the life of Chequers.

Thanksgiving. How much has Chequers given to the community over the last 42 years! Dr David Cruikshank and Euan Martin have reminded us so well of so many good memories. There is no need for me to repeat any of that. I simply suggest we put all of what they so eloquently said in the context of thanksgiving, or gratitude. So many residents cared for. So many families helped. So much employment given. So much voluntary energy channelled into worthy and worthwhile efforts. Truly the life of Chequers has been a blessing to many individuals, to many families, to the life of Pitlochry and the surrounding communities. So, the first note we strike in a service like this is one of gratitude to God for all that he has given us through the life and work of Chequers. Gratitude.

So, first Thanksgiving, but then hard on its heels comes Sadness, or perhaps even Grief. Something we have loved has been lost, and it is right and natural to express our sorrow. Sometimes we feel a bit buttoned up about saying that we are sad, but in many circumstances, sadness is a right and proper reaction. Quite naturally, when something comes to an end, we feel a sense of loss. But where better to express our sorrow than here in the house of God? – for God knows what we feel, and God understands. God cares, and he can help us in our time of sorrow, so we should not hesitate to express our sadness to him.

Sometimes people feel that Thanksgiving and Grief are odd bed-fellows. They are such opposing feelings – how can they go together? The answer I think is that Thanksgiving and Grief are two sides of the one coin. If we had not been glad for the life of Chequers, why would we be sorry when it comes to an end? We can only be sad about losing something, if we were glad when we had it. So, though Thanksgiving and Grief seem to be such different emotions they go together cheek by jowl, and it is right that we express them both, together, side by side, when someone or something that we love, dies. And so, we have Thanksgiving *and* Grief together.

And thirdly, and lastly, and I would say, most importantly, we come to Faith. We take our Thanksgiving in one hand, and we take our Sadness in the other, and here, in the house of God, we gather them up and place them into the care of Almighty God, who loves us, and who cares for us, and whose good purposes for us can never come to an end.

What in particular does the Christian faith tell us at a time like this? I suggest it tells us that nothing that is given to God can ever be truly lost. Rather, the things that we give to God will last for ever.

We read from Mark 8. There in verse 35 we read that disturbing but profoundly true saying of Jesus, *"Whoever wants to save his own life will lose it; but whoever loses his life for me and for the gospel will save it".* There Jesus tells us the paradoxical truth that the things that we cling to ourselves, we lose; but the things that we give away we actually keep.

The quotation I have used as my sermon title, and which is printed on the Order of Service, takes this saying of Jesus, and applies it to our own deaths. *"The only things we take with us from our life on earth are those which we have given away."* When we die it is stating the obvious that we cannot take with us the things that we have accumulated for ourselves: our money, our possessions, our clothes, our valuables. And the paradoxical truth is that it is the good things that we have given away that are the things that we will take with us into our new life with God: kindness, compassion, thoughtfulness, mercy, forgiveness – love.

We also read from Micah 6. There the prophet tells us that God wants us *"to do what is just, to show constant love, and to live in humble fellowship with our God".* Another translation puts it this way: God requires of us that we *"do justice, and love kindness".* *"To show constant love, ... and to love kindness."* Has Chequers not been a place where, with the help of God, and in the name of Christ, love has been shown, and kindness has been demonstrated?

Love, kindness, mercy: these are the things that have been given away over the last 42 years in Chequers. So, these things will not be lost. It is the things that we cling to ourselves that we lose; but the things that we give away last forever.

The official closing date for Chequers is this coming Wednesday, which is why I have put that date on the Order of Service sheet. Chequers, the Church of Scotland Care Home, is coming to an end. But the things that have been given away there will endure: the care that has been shown, the acts of kindness that have been offered, the friendships that have been forged. Those things, in the providence of God will last. And so that completes the third part of what we mark in this service today. There is Gratitude. There is Sorrow. But binding these two together, and holding them up to God, there is Faith. There is the faith that with God the things of value will last, and the faith that what Chequers has given away will endure. *"The only things we take with us from our life on earth are those which we have given away."* Amen.

Hymn 726 (Somos del Senor)
When we are living, we are in the Lord

Prayers of Thanksgiving
To be led by Annie McDonald, Head of Older People's Services (North)
(CrossReach)

Almighty God, Father of mercies and fountain of all goodness, we praise you for all your gifts to us through the years. We thank you for the blessings of life and health and strength. We thank you for all the affections, friendships and love we meet in our daily life; and for the tasks and responsibilities by which we are involved, as Christ's people, in the lives of others. God grant us such a lively sense of your goodness that we may devote ourselves to your will and service, so that, loving you, we may find the way to an increasing love and brotherhood among all your children.

O loving God, who has led us to ways of service as individuals and as a Christian community: We rejoice this day, in the caring ministry of Chequers, where the virtues of Christ, and his command to love God and our neighbour, were made manifest in the devoted care of the elderly. For every man and woman, once resident in Chequers, who found there, contentment and peace, care, and compassion, we give you thanks. For all who worked in the Home: ministering to the elderly as to Christ Himself, and who, in spite of the sadness of this day, can hear your words, *"Well done, good and faithful servant"* – For each one of them,

193

and for all that they did to care in Christ's name, we give you thanks. For the fond remembrances of all of us who had some part in the life of the Home, great or small, we bring you our thanks, O God. *Lord, in your mercy, hear our prayer.*

(The Choir sings the Response: *'O Lord hear my prayer'* (Taizé Community).

Prayers of Intercession
To be led by Mary Russell, elder for Chequers,
and member of the Circle of Friends, 2001-2009

Good and kind God, hear our prayer for those, late of Chequers, now resident in other Homes. Grant them peace and joy in their lives, and the certain knowledge that the Christ in whose name they were cared for at Chequers, loves and cares for them still.

We pray for members of staff, now in employment elsewhere, or still seeking employment, that they too may be conscious of the love of God, which is constant, even in a changing world.

Hear the prayer of those of us who· were Friends of Chequers, in every guise, and every avenue of service. To be associated with the Home has brought deep enrichment to our lives. That we have been permitted to share in this caring work has been an immense privilege.

May we be better servants of our Lord and Saviour, Jesus Christ, because of our experience in this Home.

We pray dear God that you will bless all of your children, who are in any kind of need today.

Grant them the assurance that they are loved, and remembered, and that their needs will be met. Enable Christian people everywhere to respond to the needs of humanity wherever they see them, that your will may be done.

Lord, in your mercy, hear our prayer.

(The Choir sings the Response: 'O lord hear my prayer' (Taizé Community)).

The Lord's Prayer
To be led by Revd Malcolm Ramsay

HYMN 153 (Faithfulness)
Great is thy faithfulness, O God my Father
BENEDICTION (sung Amen)
The congregation are asked to remain seated for

Sung Blessing by Choir
May the Lord always bless you

Retiring Organ Voluntary: Fugue in E Flat Major, (St Anne), by J. S. Bach. (Organist: Eddie Allan)
Following the service all are warmly invited to the Tryst for refreshments, and to share memories of Chequers with each other

Memories of Chequers – Mrs Ruth Boa
Chequers opened in 1966, The accommodation provided for 36 residents in shared rooms, which gave great companionship and support. There was no night staff for many years. Resident staff were on call during the night.

Over the years, Chequers built up the life and work of the home, enabling many elderly residents and their families to enjoy life, with many staff and volunteers sharing in that life.

Chequers also became involved in the life of the young in the area, visits from schools including Pitlochry, Aberfeldy, Logierait, Blair Atholl and Struan giving opportunities for mutual learning. Rannoch School also enjoyed the residents' and staff's memories for History and Modern Studies.

We were honorary members of the local Scouts and Guides and enjoyed 'camp fires' in Chequers lounge as well as working towards the badge scheme. We were also involved with the Duke of Edinburgh Awards scheme, allowing those involved in the awards to carry out certain tasks to gain their badges.

The local Sunday School donated a Lectern from their 'save-a-penny' scheme.

Later staff became involved in Community Service for offenders asking residents to show these people a valuable way to live their lives, and their continued contact proved that.

Many of the daily activities included news groups, quizzes, bingo, baking (showing up lots of rivalry, especially on scones), polishing silver, and handbags, sewing and other crafts were also included. However, the recall groups were greatly valued.

Annual events were celebrated – birthdays, Christmas, Hogmanay, Burns Supper and Easter.

Chequers had a very special relationship with the Pipe Band and became a 'Good Luck' charm; a pipe tune called *'Tribute to Chequers'* was composed to celebrate the Year of the Elderly.

The Saturday night dance music and a waltz round the lounge was a ritual for residents and staff.

Visitors were vital and shared by many in the lounge, often families chatting to each other; privacy could always be had in their own rooms. In the early days, pets, i.e., dogs, cats, rabbits, lambs and ferrets, were welcomed, which resulted in an award from the Cinnamon Trust, recognising the therapeutic value of animals.

The Senior Citizens Bus gave freedom to travel to many less able residents – picnics, day trips, theatres, pantomimes, concerts and galleries.

There was always time set aside for quietness, worship and meditation, with daily prayers, Sunday service and reflection on funerals.

Staff development was vital, including SVQ, in-house training and learning 'off-site'. One of the greatest credits to them was that we pioneered Day Care and Respite Care in the home before the Tryst was born.

Fund raising for the home was vital, but in turn we contributed to fund raising for others including The Tryst, Pipe Band, Radio Heartland, Meningitis Trust and Churches. None of this would have been possible without the help of volunteers of all aspects of life, including voluntary optician service at Chequers when there was none in Pitlochry. We also had the Chequers Community Club.

Memories of Chequers – Mrs Helen McNicoll

Chequers was a happy place to work in and hopefully to live in.

Staff who came to *"help out for a couple of weeks"* were still there twenty years later.

Entertainment was a major part of life with visitors from playgroup with their Nativity play through guides, school concerts, actors from the Festival Theatre to the entire cast of Strathblair which was filmed locally.

Women's Guilds from the area would come to entertain and often there were competitions such as Easter Bonnets, some of which were weird and wonderful.

Other competitions held were growing tomatoes on the windowsills of the lounge or spring bulbs in the bedrooms.

There was great rivalry.

The community bus was used a lot to go on different outings. In spring we ventured out to see the lambs in the fields and in autumn to see the colours of the trees. In winter we went to Perth to do Christmas shopping.

Longer trips were held in the summer and we went as far as Nairn, Inverness Highland Wildlife Park and Balmoral.

Only a few residents stayed at home.

We had lots of visitors, from the weekly hairdresser, chiropodist, optician and a physiotherapist who came to help give individual advice and encourage music and movement. Staff also helped with music and movement, and once when taken to a concert in a church hall, when the dance band started playing, the residents started to do their routine. Staff accompanying them were mortified.

The TV was often the source of a battle of wills to decide what would be watched. One lady who was a keen viewer would keep the remote control on her chair and if something came on which the majority wanted, she would change the channel until they all left the room and then put whatever she wanted. Another three would book their front row seats with library book or shawls and woe betide anyone who sat in these chairs.

When residents began to have their own TVs in their rooms, this solved a lot of problems.

Another source of delight was the visit of a firm which came twice a year with clothes for both men and women. A whole morning was spent trying on lots of new things with relatives sometimes coming in to assist. The night staff had the job of sewing on all the name tapes.

Once we received instructions from Head Office that residents were not to sit round the room. 'Too institutionalised' the message was relayed to residents who reluctantly agreed to give it a go.

Staff took two hours rearranging chairs and tables so that everyone sat near their friends and as near to their preferred place as possible. Next morning it took two residents fifteen minutes to put it all back. *"We are not having this!"*

They couldn't see what was going on unless they were round the room and some would give a running commentary on what staff were doing.

Christmas was a hectic time with parties and going out to concerts. Residents were asked to get their Christmas cards written and presents bought by early Dec. One lady refused to do this, preferring to wait until she had received a card or present, when she would send her key worker up to the shops to get a card to send back. This went on all through December!

For his birthday one man asked for a clootie dumpling *"all to myself"*. The cook duly obliged and he enjoyed his tea that night.

There were lots of other events, excitement and arguments so this is just a small example of life in Chequers.

Memories of Chequers – Rita Isles

I was privileged to work as a hairdresser in Chequers for a good number of years. I worked one day a week, on a Tuesday – trims, shampoo & sets, blow dries, perms, plus manicures and hand massage which worked in two ways – they either fell asleep or had the giggles, especially with the hand massage. Overall, it was a great way of hearing stories of the past and how life was in earlier years, and some of the ladies and gents who came from further afield told of getting the steamer from Aberdeen to London as it was cheaper than the train and, although it was mainly a cargo boat, they had their own cabins, a dining room, and ceilidhs and dances on their journey which took a night and a day and was a holiday in itself even if the water was turbulent.

I discovered an onion was an 'ingin' from an old north-east lady, and an old gamekeeper told me pheasants were suicidal: *"If an owl flew in, the young pheasants would appear to queue up to be killed by a peck on the head from the owl"*. So, this is why young birds are enclosed in cages to enable them to mature and hopefully protect them from foxes who also kill for the sake of killing.

Another lady I chatted with turned out to be connected to my part of South Ayrshire. Her husband was the grandson of John McAdam who experimented with tarmacadam and put this substance on a short stretch of road in my home town of Maybole, which I knew to be correct as it was a story told to me when I was young, and how the tar melted on a hot day, frustrating many locals until the ironmonger on the corner discovered that paraffin would clean away the tar from shoes and clothes. The road is still there, and a few layers down is the original tar surface.

This lady who was married to John McAdam's grandson was also a fascinating fount of information on the theatre and music hall artists, as she worked most of her life in Carlyle Theatre in the box office, and her memories were extensive.

Being in the background, I could often join in the activities happening after I had done my bit (hairdressing). It was always fun with the staff and visitors always joining in and so many talented local people going in for a couple of hours with music, singalongs, and demonstrations. Also, trips out were arranged with the community bus, picnics, afternoon tea, art exhibitions, the residents sat outside in the very well-manicured garden in their sun hats and watched the world go by.

Report Sent to Local Papers – Ruth Boa

In celebration of summer and 37 years of service to the community, Chequers held a summer cameo on Thursday 7th August 2003. This took the form of a cameo of medieval costumes designed by Rita Isles who is a friend and supporter of the home and talented dressmaker & historian.

The ladies of the group were Mrs Fiona McPherson and her daughters Caroline who was celebrating her seventh birthday and Iona who is three years. They thrilled the assembled crowd with a parade of their striking gowns and incredible period Plantagenet hats with butterfly veils. The residents and visitors were also delighted to see their period posies of rosemary, thyme, mint & lavender. Rita's husband Donald also demonstrated a very striking period costume wearing his medieval family crest on his houppelande (tunic).

Patchwork Costume parade 2003. From left: Fiona McPherson with daughters Iona and Caroline, and Donald Isles.

The afternoon's splendour was recorded for the scrapbooks by 'Lady Fiona's' son Ruaridh McPherson. A delightful summer tea was served by the home's staff and members of the friends group had a small stall for home funds raising £300.

THE TRYST DAY CARE CENTRE

Memories of Betty Condie

"The Tryst Day Care Centre opened on 4th September 1996; the building was dedicated to the Glory of God by the then Moderator the Right Revd John McIndoe MA, BD, STM, and serves many church groups as a place for retreat or conference as well as allowing individual groups to hire various parts of the building for social events, i.e., birthdays, coffee mornings, table tennis, Scottish country dancing and many more occasions. However, it became clear that for some people living alone or with only one carer or with minimal outside help, there was a need for companionship, and also a day or so for the carer or family member to have free time. Perth & Kinross local authority decided to give financial support for a day care centre for the elderly, which opened in January 1998. On the first day there were just three clients, but this very quickly built up to the maximum of sixteen.

The 'Senior Citizens' bus with a volunteer driver picked up most of the clients; others from much further afield arrived by taxi. All usually arrived by 10.00 am.

On arrival, clients would be served tea and toast, which was most appreciated in cold weather. The rest of the morning was taken up with a news group when the daily papers were read out and The Courier crossword duly completed. There was usually knitting and sewing going on at the same time. Staff, at times, also did bathing in the morning and afternoon.

Lunch was collected from the school kitchen during term time and Chequers during school holidays and served at tables – usually soup and main course or main and pudding. All dishes and kitchen tidy up was also done by the staff.

Afternoons were spent doing some sort of exercise and games activities which were enjoyable, before going home at 4.00pm after tea and cakes were served. A staff member escorted the clients on the bus home.

These happy days were very busy for the two staff members as we had no volunteer help other than drivers and morning escort.

Two highlights for me would be that we were used as a pilot for the Church of Scotland day-care throughout the country, and the other was that we worked to such a high standard that the Social Work Department allowed us to do our own entry assessments at that time."

Memories of Christine Campbell

"How much the clients enjoyed their day; the men talked about going to work – they were always busy with lots of chatter. The ladies were busy knitting and lots of activities. It gave them so much pleasure. We had sixteen clients, three days a week."

Memories of the Author

"As a stand in for either of the staff going on holiday or sick, I enjoyed the challenge of keeping up with the wit and my arty side. Again, I picked up on stories of the past and used my hairdressing skills.

There were many laughs reading out newspaper items, especially when someone had not heard correctly. My biggest nightmare was reading out the lottery numbers with their equivalent wee quotes, for example, legs eleven – never did get the hang of all the numbers even with all the prompting from the clients.

The biggest success on the game front was introducing the clients to Scrabble, which was unbelievably popular. This happened just before afternoon tea. It was so popular that the bus drivers, escorts, and taxi drivers came in early so they could join in. It was hard work sending everyone home as every game had to be finished.

Playing whist or dominoes was also a challenge as many had their own interpretation of the rules. Christmas and birthdays were also great fun days, sometimes with chaos as nothing happened on time.

The job of escort could be an adventure – finding the client was locked out, their key had gone missing, trying to stay upright with a client on your arm while walking on ice, guiding a new driver on the routes we took, having a singsong and forgetting to stop at certain houses, finding the ramp had broken down at a critical time when the bus was blocking the road.

It was exhausting but it was years never to be forgotten."

Pitlochry Senior Citizens Good Neighbour Association

Until 1980, Pitlochry and the surrounding areas had a minibus (people carrier) that helped the ambulant senior people to get around and about and meet up with people of a similar age. A newspaper article of February 1979 explained.

Self Help is Aim of OAP Scheme

An effort is being made to bring Pitlochry's senior residents, numbering about 500, closer together in mutual self help. A committee of reference has been set up in connection with the project. Dr David Cruikshank is chairman, and the Rev Bill Shannon of Moulin & Pitlochry West Church, is secretary.

Mrs D. McRobbie is already the organiser of the Senior Citizens Day Club, which meets on Tuesday and Thursday in the West Church hall.

'The First Bus', 12th July 1980.

Opened two years ago, it has almost 50 regular members and is in contact with a further 50 people.

It became clear to the Rev Bill Shannon and Dr David Cruikshank that transport was needed which would have easy access, with room to move about in, and a hydraulic tailgate for wheelchairs. The bus would transport to and from the Senior Citizens Day Club. It would also operate for organised shopping trips, social outings, church and hospital visits, and clinic attendances.

A bid to raise funds for the vehicle then got under way. Their aim was to purchase a second-hand bus which they hoped would be available in April 1979 for £1,200. The Committee comprised:

'Presenting the First Bus', 12th July 1980.
Left: Revd Bill Shannon (Secretary), right: Dr David Cruikshank (Chairman).

Chairman	Dr D. A. Cruikshank
Secretary	Revd W. Shannon
Treasurer	A. S. Cowie, Esq, CA
Old Peoples' Welfare Committee	Mrs A. Grant
Matron, IMH	Mrs R. Ripley
Tuesday Club	Mrs M. McLeod
Tayside Regional Education Department	Mrs D. McRobbie

There were also representatives in turn from the Tuesday Club, Probus Club and Round Table, Pitlochry.

The Revd Bill Shannon was so excited that he persuaded Dr D. Cruikshank to go and see the proposed bus 'out of hours' in Edinburgh, so fences were climbed to view it! It was large and cumbersome, but it was what was needed.

The target for the bus was £1,200. The fund-raising project raised

£2,500 locally and a further £3,000 in grants, plus a late donation of £600 from Help the Aged, which would cover maintenance, and guarantee that the vehicle be on the road for some time.

All this was achieved in four months. An informal ceremony outside Fishers Hotel took place on Saturday 12th July 1980, and the following day, the bus was in action on Sunday morning for church runs, starting at the fountain in front of the Royal Bank of Scotland at 10.15. It went round the town, picking up passengers for the 11.00 services. One of the first drivers was Daphne McRobbie, who was told if you can drive a tractor then you can drive the bus. Daphne is a farmer's wife.

The bus was put to great use, including raising funds for bus number 2 in 1982. In May 1982, plans were put in place to raise funds for the new bus; the target figure was £20,000. Daphne McRobbie was organising fund raising events along with the committee. Pitlochry & District Round Table presented a cheque for £500 to the Pitlochry Senior Citizens new minibus appeal at their Gala Day in August 1982.

Fund raising continued with special draws at the Atholl Palace, market stalls, sales of books, Highland afternoons in the Recreation Ground, musical shows, concert parties, jumble sales, coffee mornings and many donations and support from local organisations. In less than six months, by 2nd October 1982, £7,000 had been raised. On 15th November 1982, with financial help from Help the Aged, the Duke of Atholl (Ian Murray) received the keys of a new bus from Mr Graham Lale, assistant director of development for Help the Aged.

Although Help the Aged supplied half of the capital cost, the vehicle belonged to the Senior Citizens Association. The bus was luxuriously equipped; it featured a hydraulic tailgate which allowed the more disabled and wheelchair-bound people to get on board and to become mobile and integrated with the community.

£8,000 had been raised in six months; the other half was provided by Help the Aged. This was the 107th bus to be handed over to communities in the last two years. Some of the first drivers were Tom Donaldson, Ian McIntosh, and Bill Ripley. The bus was a new Volkswagen LT 12-seater.

The move towards a new bus came about in April 1982 when Daphne McRobbie advised the Committee of Reference that a new vehicle would be needed by the end of 1982.

The original target figure was £20,000, but with Help the Aged becoming involved, this was trimmed to £15,000. Mr Graham Lale received a cheque from the Pitlochry association which he explained would go back into the bus fund so that Help the Aged can help another similar organisation somewhere in the UK. Mr Lale also explained that Help the Aged buy the buses direct from Volkswagen and have them converted by a Southampton firm. They are then driven to their destination. The new bus arrived on 15th November 1982.

Fund raising for the bus has continued over the years enabling the buses to be renewed or repaired.

Annually there is a coffee morning, and there is also a local Christmas card delivery service. All the people involved are volunteers.

The Chairmen of the Association have been:

David Cruikshank   June 1979-1985
Ruby Ripley   1985-2004
Donald Isles   2004-2010
Linda Moyes   2010-

'The Third Bus' – Ruby Ripley (Matron) and Ian Mcintosh (driver)
receiving the bus at the Irvine Memorial Hospital c.1987.

The Second to Last Bus, February 2010 –
David Clark (of John R. Weir) and Donald Isles (Chairman).

Bobbin Mill

The Bobbin Mill locale was a busy area for small industries at different times in the past, as well as being a smallholding area for farming. Before the railway embankment was built, the area of Bobbin Mill was visible from the Main Road, now named Atholl Road (named by the town council in November 1954). The north side of the railway next to Atholl Road was a market garden, where Pitlochry War Memorial and Garden is now.

Bobbin Mill was a turning mill which produced tent pegs and bobbins which were sent to the Indian Jute Mills. The wood used was birch, of which there was a plentiful supply locally. Bobbin Mill was built in 1893 and was owned by Mrs Taylor and managed by Mr Stewart. In 1896, Bobbin Mill had to move further westward into the woods, an area just beyond the house on the left of the road to Pitlochry Community Hospital. The mill stayed there until it burnt down in 1926. The move was to allow new gasholders to be built as the previous gasholders on Bonnethill Road, next to Scotland's Hotel, were not adequate. The new gasholders held 30,000 cubic feet and allowed for many more street lights and for houses to have gas lighting. Balfour and Company of Leven built the gasholders at a cost of £2,000. In the late 1980s, these gas holders were removed and eventually the area was made into two car parks.

There was a sawmill beside the railway bridge which also used birch to make charcoal for gunpowder. This area was sometimes referred to as the 'Chemical Works'. A second sawmill stood where the restaurant opposite the bridge traffic lights is today. The sawmill supplied fuels of wood, peat, charcoal, and coal. Another industry based on local timber supply involved the cutting of birch twigs in the woods for making birch brooms used in the manufacture of steel.

Epilogue
Some Thoughts

SCOTLAND'S COMMUNITIES have been privileged to have cottage/
community hospitals in the hinterland of cities. Without them and their
like, the city hospitals would quickly fill up with cases of elderly patients
whose relatives of all ages would find it difficult to visit.

There is something a little quaint about the term 'Cottage Hospital'
and also the long-forgotten dignitaries after whom they were often
named. It is wrong to consider them a respite centre, as they are good
stepping stones for patients after surgery or illness when they are too
well for main hospitals but not quite ready for home. Physiotherapy,
occupational therapy, and professional nursing care are on hand, and
the confidence this can give patients helps them return home.

Large hospitals are becoming increasingly blind to the needs of individual
patients and are discharging folk too early, leaving GPs to pick up the pieces.

Patients and families consider it important to be close to home and
family as there is comfort to be gained from this situation.

Cottage hospitals are constantly under threat of closure due to purse
strings tightening. The 'money men' of the health boards do not understand
there will always be quieter times in cottage hospitals compared to large
city hospitals. Is 'bed blocking' partly due to a lack of cottage hospitals?

Financial costs prevent the local cottage hospital from having
facilities like x-ray, minor surgery, and paper work and a fear of being
sued inhibit many basic treatments that Dr Irvine had no choice but to do.

Minor casualty facilities do exist during working hours, when they
can suture and dress wounds when of a less serious nature and decide
if closer supervision is required in a city hospital.

Many people of senior years recall how they had their tonsils
extracted on the kitchen table, or children delivered in the same room
they all lived in – and they survived.

Safety and modern techniques and practices prevent our return to
those days, but our cottage hospitals can still work within a local rural
community with a very beneficial effect on local and outlying areas.

THE PUBLISHER

Tippermuir Books Ltd (*est.* 2009) is an independent
publishing company based in Perth, Scotland.

OTHER TITLES FROM
TIPPERMUIR BOOKS

Spanish Thermopylae (Paul S. Philippou, 2009)

Battleground Perthshire
(Paul S. Philippou & Robert A. Hands, 2009)

Perth: Street by Street
(Paul S. Philippou and Roben Antoniewicz, 2012)

Born in Perthshire
(Paul S. Philippou and Robert A. Hands, 2012)

In Spain with Orwell (Christopher Hall, 2013)

Trust (Ajay Close, 2014)

Perth: As Others Saw Us (Donald Paton, 2014)

Love All (Dorothy L. Sayers, 2015)

A Chocolate Soldier (David W. Millar, 2016)

The Early Photographers of Perthshire
(Roben Antoniewicz and Paul S. Philippou, 2016)

Taking Detective Novels Seriously:
The Collected Crime Reviews of Dorothy L. Sayers
(Dorothy L. Sayers and Martin Edwards, 2017)

Walking with Ghosts (Alan J. Laing, 2017)

No Fair City: Dark Tales From Perth's Past
(Gary Knight, 2017)

The Tale o the Wee Mowdie that
wantit tae ken wha keeched on his heid
(Werner Holzwarth and Wolf Erlbruch,
translated by Matthew Mackie, 2017)

Hunters: Wee Stories from the Crescent:
A Reminiscence of Perth's Hunter Crescent
(Anthony Camilleri, 2017)

Flipstones (Jim Mackintosh, 2018)

Perth & Kinross: A Pocket Miscellany: A Companion for Visitors and Residents (Trish Colton, 2019)

God, Hitler, and Lord Peter Wimsey: Selected Essays, Speeches and Articles by Dorothy L. Sayers (Dorothy L. Sayers and Suzanne Bray (ed.), 2019)

The Piper of Tobruk: Pipe Major Robert Roy, MBE, DCM (Alice Soper, 2019)

Afore the Highlands: The Jacobites in Perth, 1715–16 (Kathleen Lyle, 2019)

FORTHCOMING

'Where Sky and Summit Meet': Flyers Over Perthshire - Tales of Pilots, Airfields, and War (Ken Bruce, 2019).

William Soutar: Collected Poetry (Kirsteen McCue and Paul S. Philippou (eds.), 2020)

BY LULLABY PRESS
(an imprint of Tippermuir Books)

A Little Book of Carol's (Carol Page, 2018)

All titles are available from bookshops and online booksellers.

They can also be purchased directly at
www.tippermuirbooks.co.uk

Tippermuir Books Ltd can be contacted at
mail@tippermuirbooks.co.uk

TIPPERMUIR
· BOOKS LIMITED ·

ABOUT THE AUTHOR

ON LEAVING SCHOOL Rita Isles planned to follow a career in science, but this did not happen the way she had hoped, so she started work as a laboratory technician for the Lord Nuffield Foundation assisting in the improvement of practical science in schools. This was followed by a few years as an orthodontic nurse, after which she moved into hospital management. After getting married, Rita changed careers again, so that she could work wherever her husband's work took them; and thus, she trained in hairdressing, first in Kirkcaldy, and then in Inverness – discovering she had also qualified as a teacher in hairdressing. Rita stayed with hairdressing and settled in Pitlochry, which led her to meeting and chatting with local people and finding out about the history of that area. Rita is also a qualified heraldic scribe.